HEINEMANN MATHEMATICS 1

Name _____

MEASURE WORKBOOK

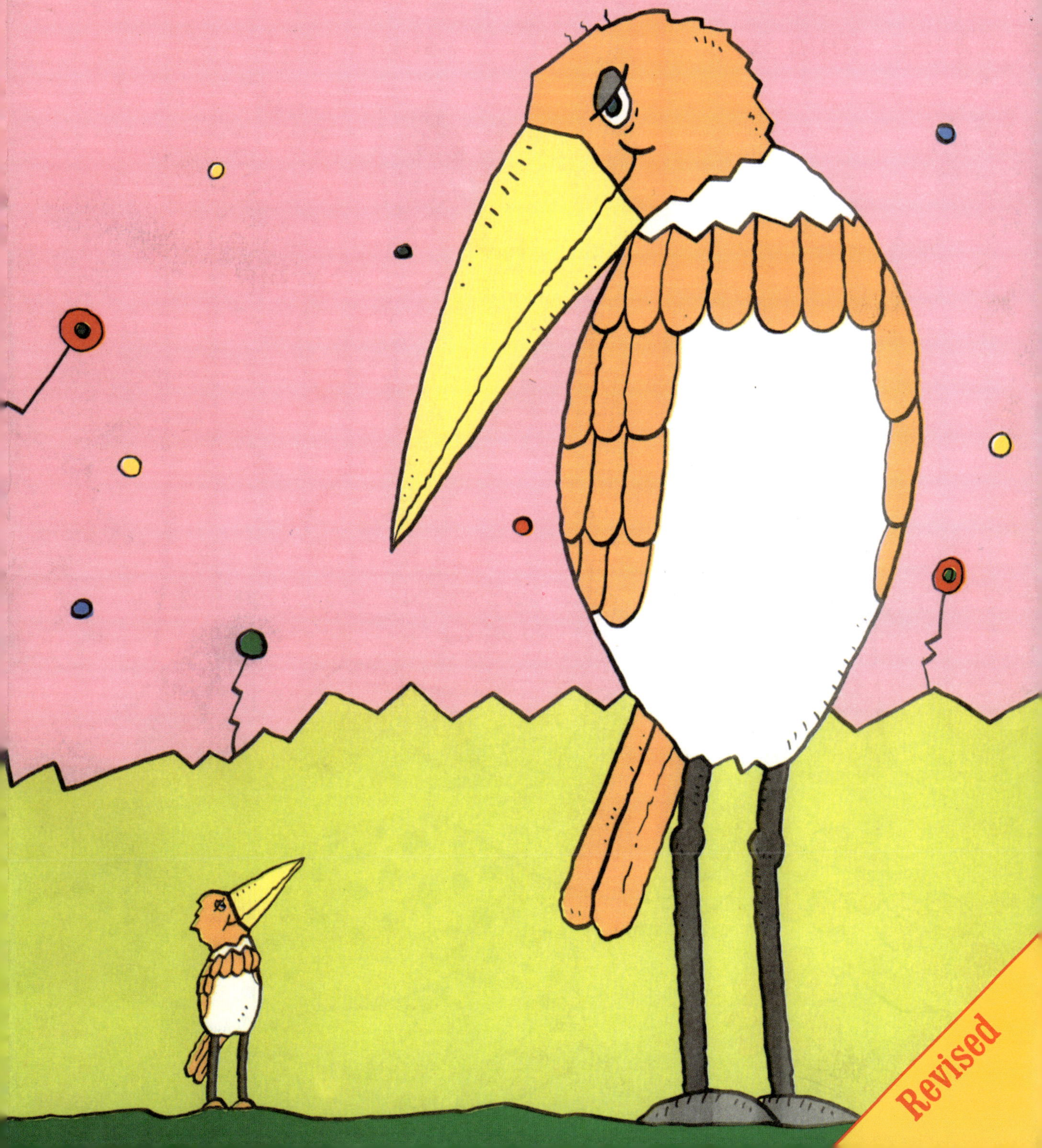

Revised

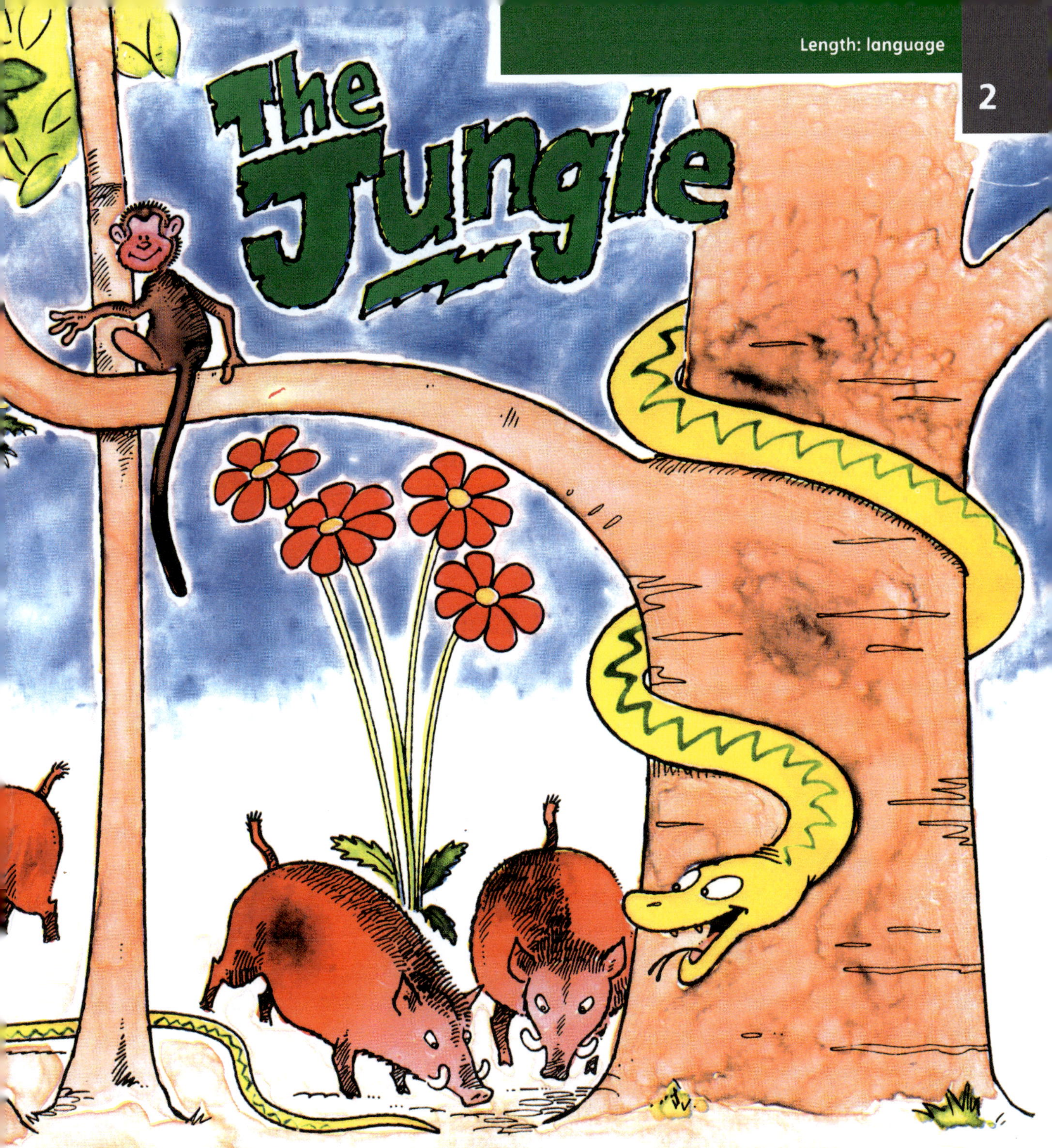

Length: language

2

The Jungle

How many:

thick trees ☐   thin trees ☐

thick snakes ☐   thin snakes ☐ ?

Day or night?

day   night

Colour the sky.

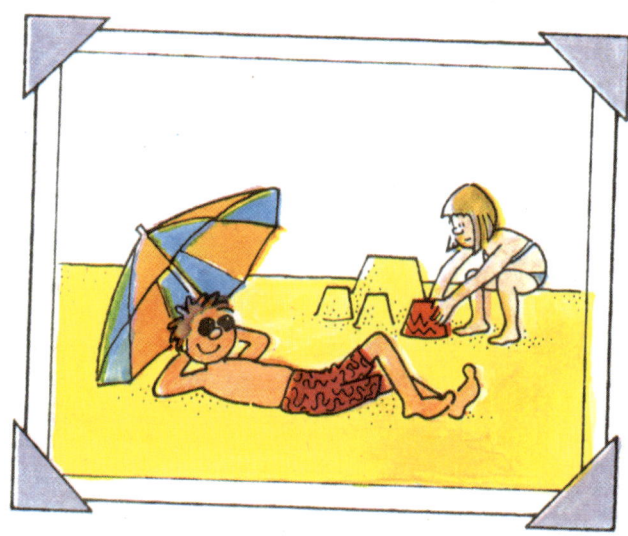

Problem solving — **Time: language**

Morning or afternoon?

Colour the morning pictures.

waking up

going home

tea time

taking in the milk

Time: language Problem solving

What happened after?

Colour

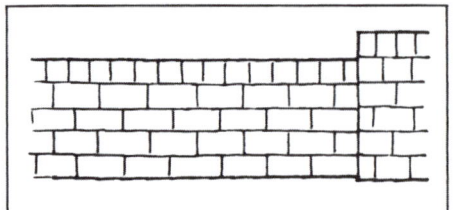

or

or

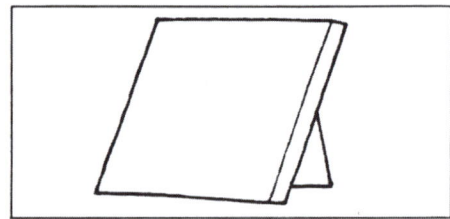

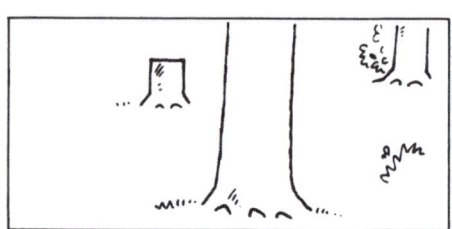

or

Problem solving   Time: language

What happened before?

Colour

or

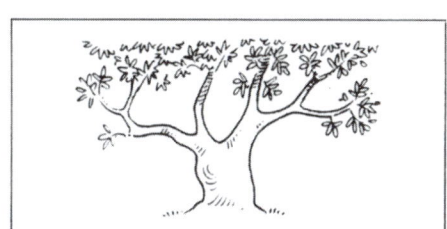
or
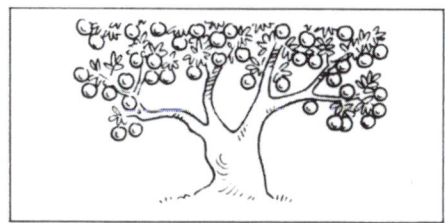

or
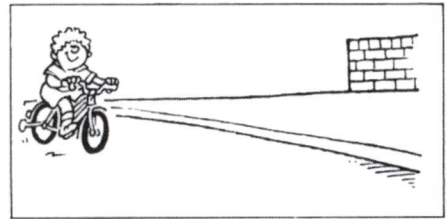

Heavier and lighter

Write **h** for heavier and **l** for lighter.

Weight: comparison

8

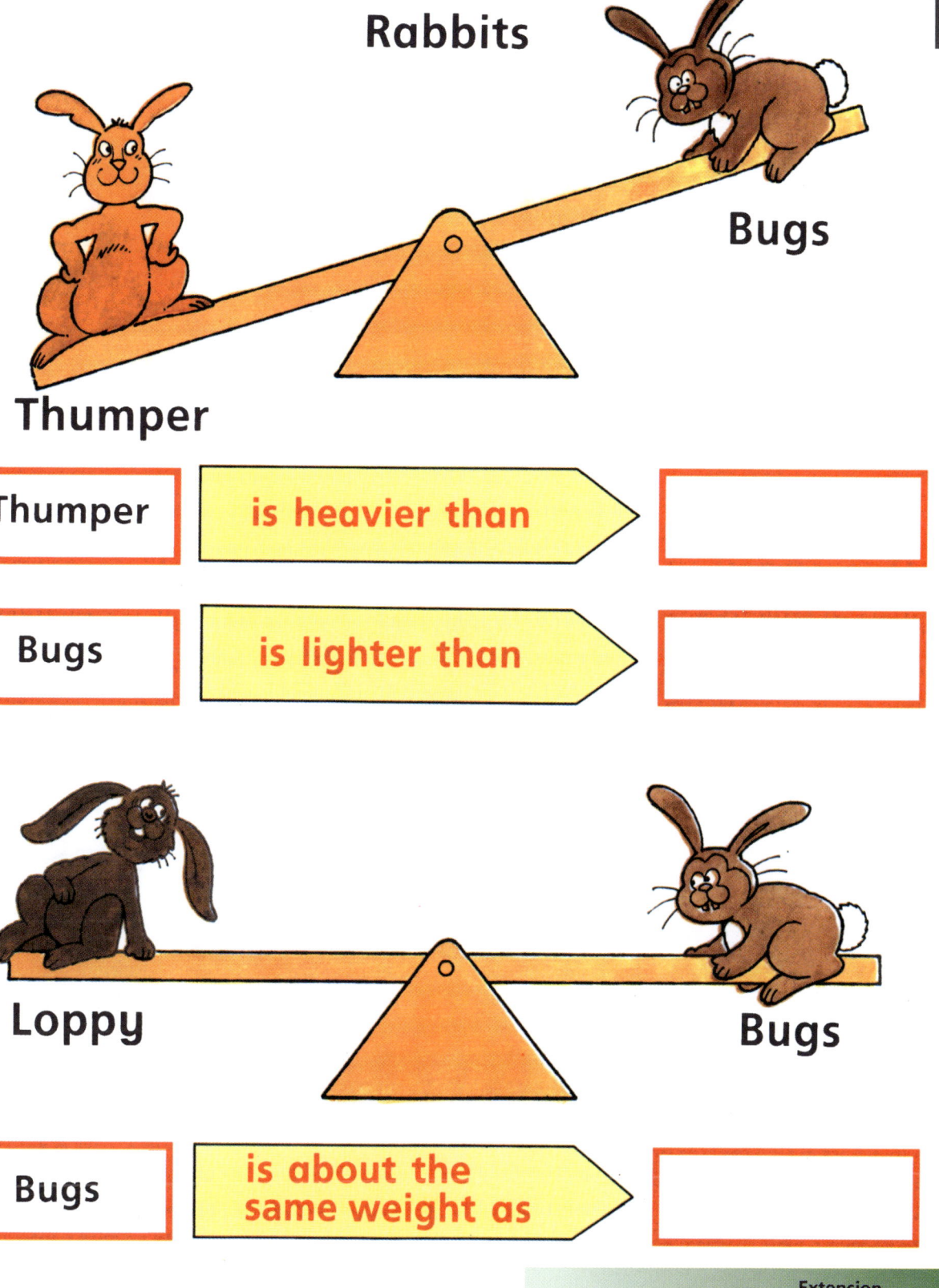

Rabbits

Thumper

| Thumper | is heavier than | |
| Bugs | is lighter than | |

| Bugs | is about the same weight as | |

Extension

| Loppy | is lighter than | |

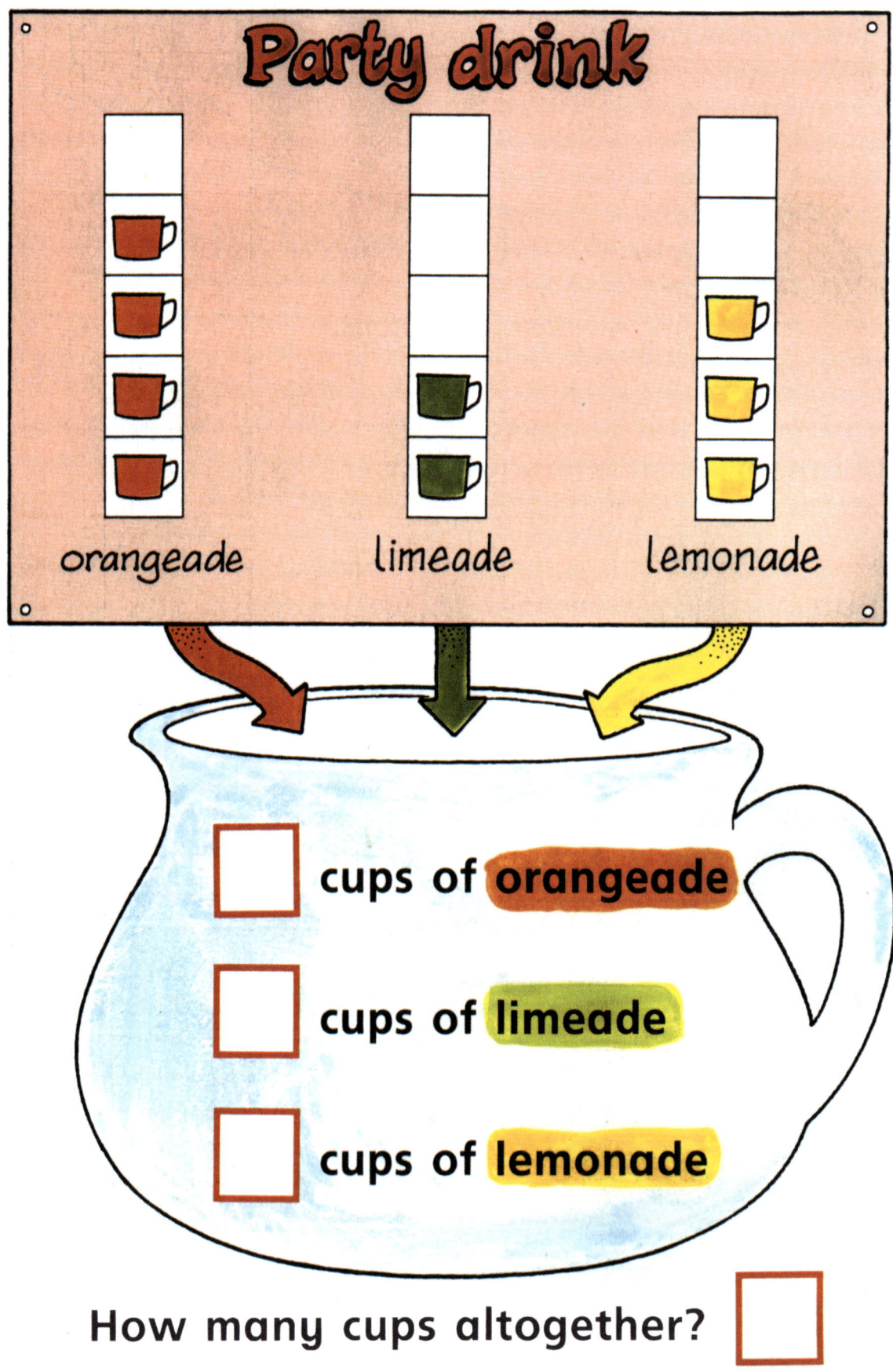

About how many cups does each fill?

Draw 🥤

Length: language

Longer and shorter

Find 2 things
longer than your thumb.

_____

_____

Find 2 things
shorter than your shoe.

_____

_____

Length: language

Taller, shorter, thicker, thinner

Find someone who is taller than you.

———————————————

Find someone who is shorter than you.

———————————————

Find something thicker than your thumb.

———————————————

Find something thinner than your little finger.

———————————————

Mark the **thicker**

Mark the **thinner**

Length: ordering

In your group who has

the longest ✏️ _____

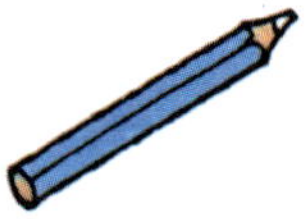

the shortest ✏️ ? _____

Colour the longest 🔴 
        the shortest 🔵

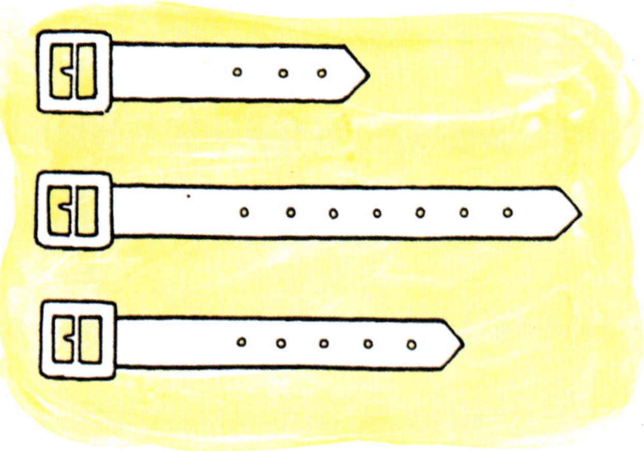

In your group who is

tallest _____

shortest? _____

Colour the tallest
the shortest

What time is it?

Time stories

Time: o'clocks

18

Time: digital display

What time is it?

☐ o'clock

☐ o'clock

☐ o'clock

☐ o'clock

Match clocks which show the same time.

Problem solving — Time

Bus times

Colour the roads the bus takes.

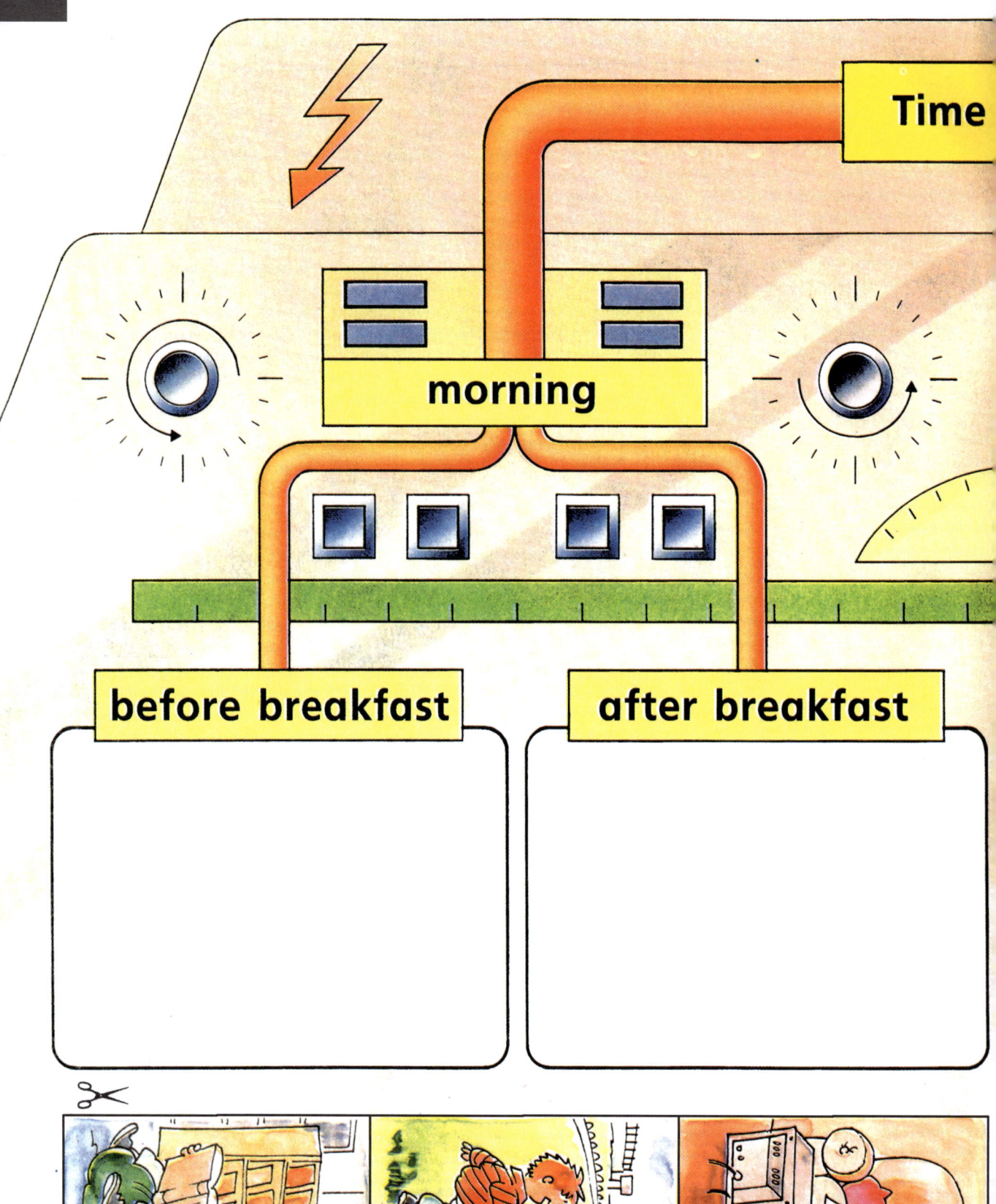

Length: comparison Group work

Shoes

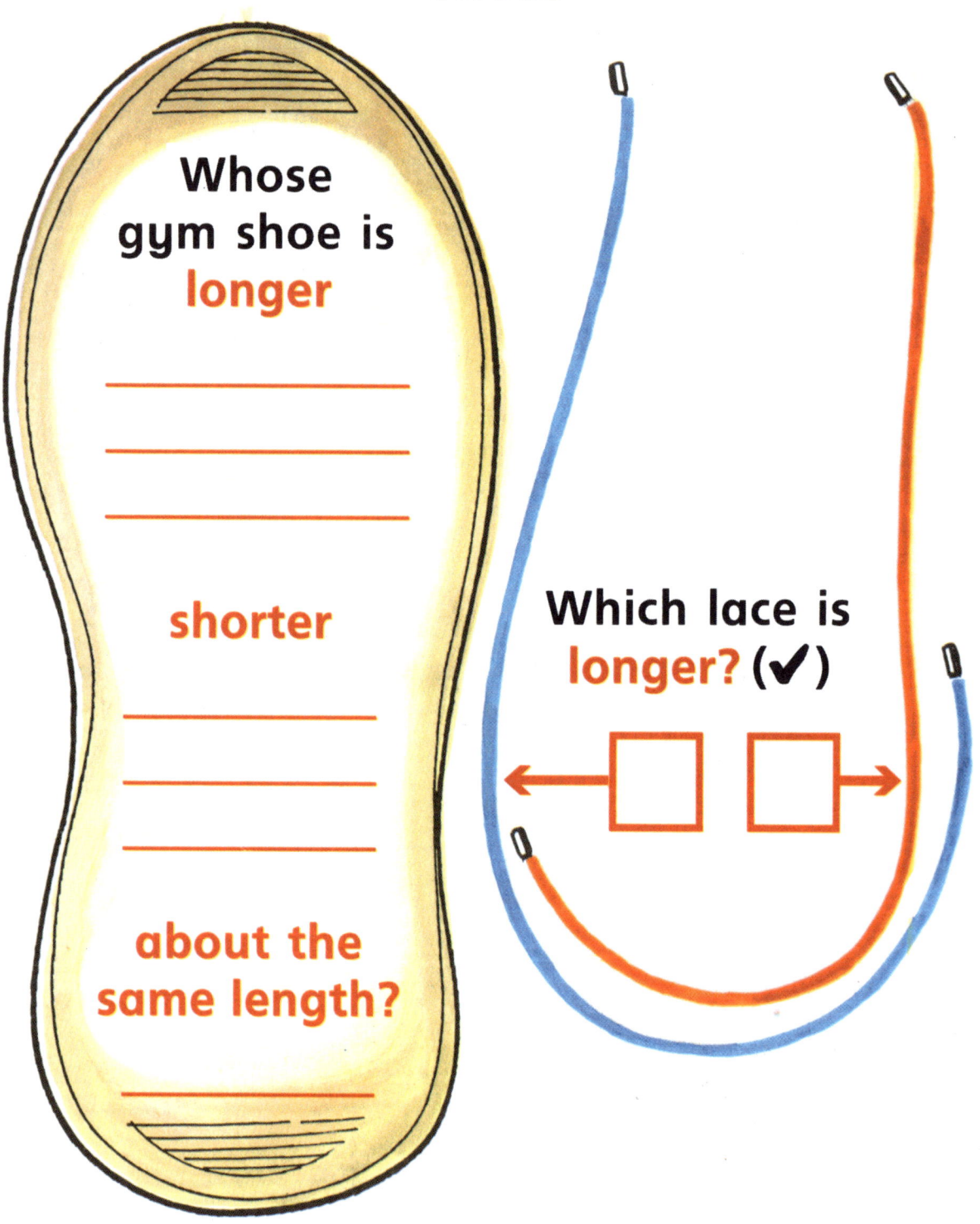

Whose gym shoe is **longer**

shorter

about the same length?

Which lace is **longer?** (✓)

SPMG

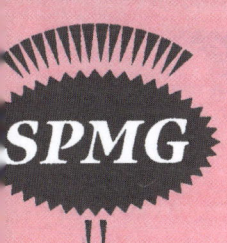

HEINEMANN MATHEMATICS 1

Name

MEASURE WORKBOOK

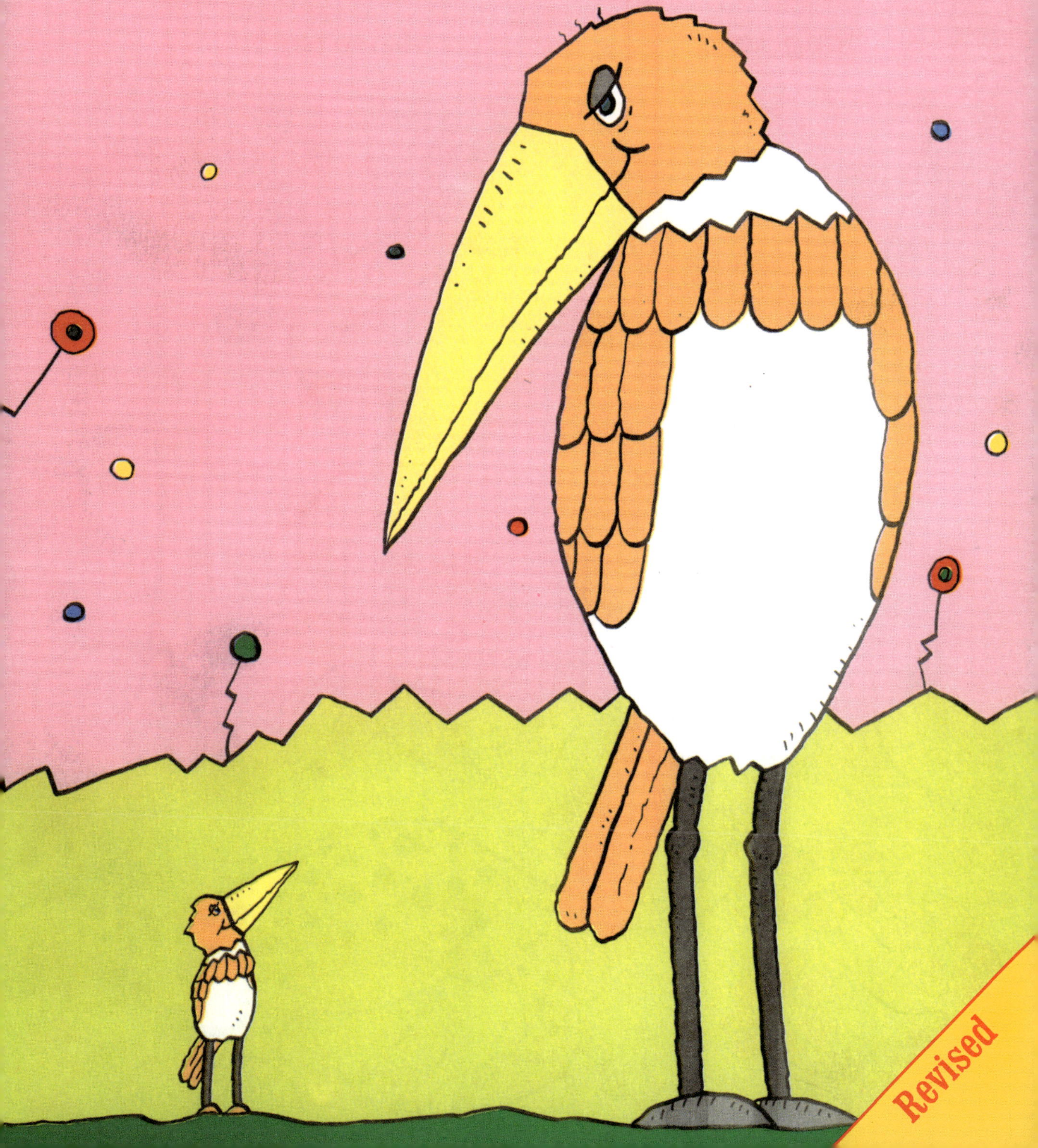

Revised

Length: language

The Jungle

How many:

thick trees ☐   thin trees ☐

thick snakes ☐   thin snakes ☐ ?

Time: language **Problem solving**

Day or night?

day　　　　　　　　　　　　　night

Colour the sky.

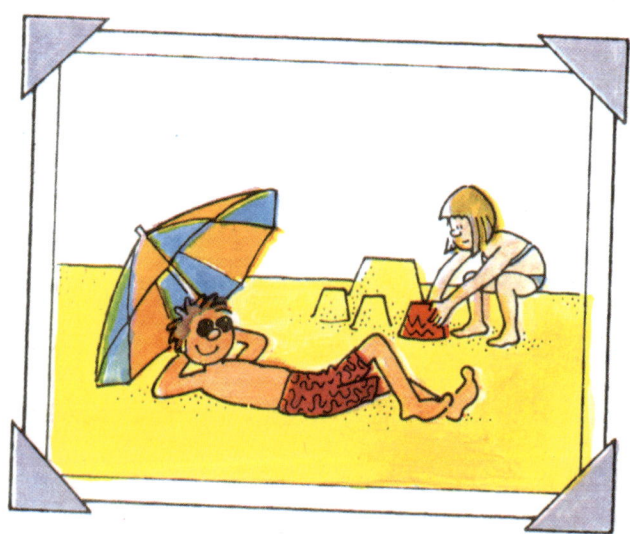

Problem solving   Time: language

Morning or afternoon?

Colour the morning pictures.

waking up

going home

tea time

taking in the milk

Time: language   Problem solving

What happened after?

Colour

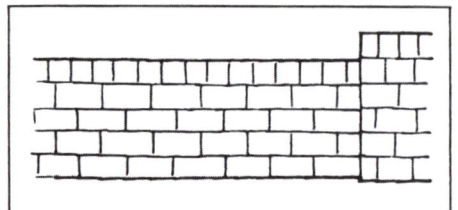

or

or

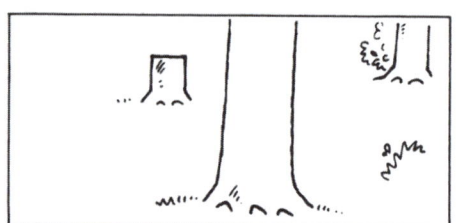

or

Problem solving   Time: language

What happened before?

Colour

or

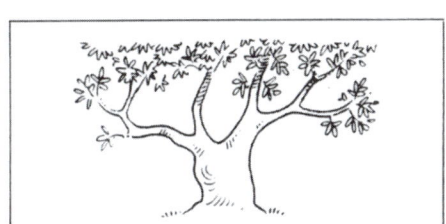

or

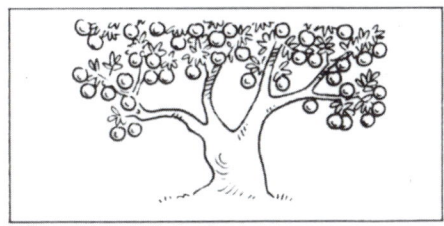

or

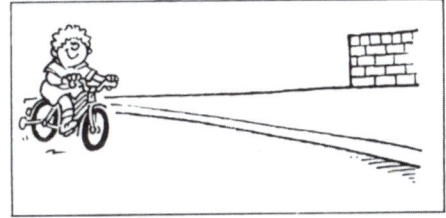

Heavier and lighter

Write [h] for heavier and [l] for lighter.

Weight: comparison

Rabbits

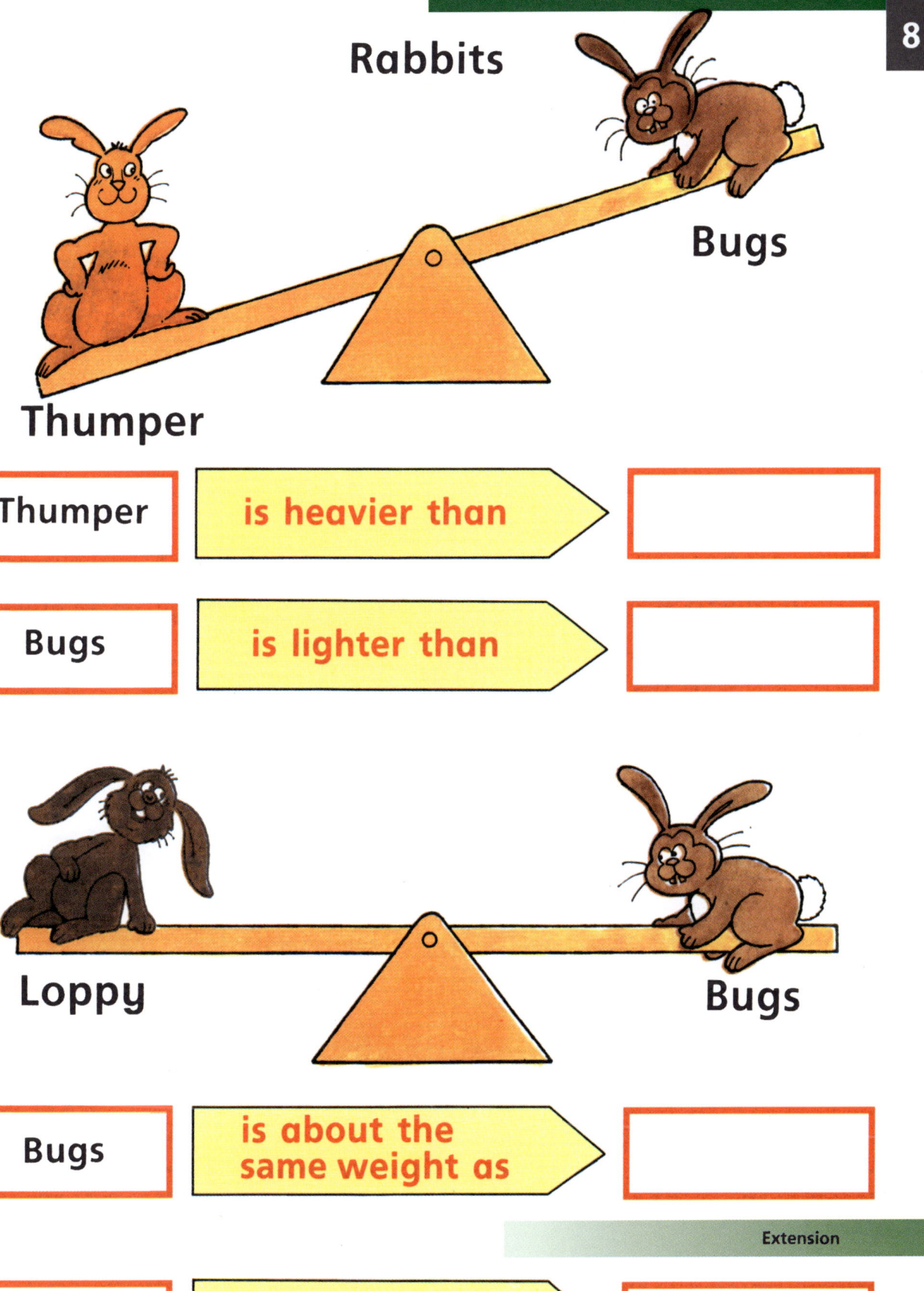

| Thumper | is heavier than | |
| Bugs | is lighter than | |

| Bugs | is about the same weight as | |

Extension

| Loppy | is lighter than | |

About how many cups does each fill?

Draw 🍵

Length: language

Longer and shorter

Find 2 things **longer** than your thumb.

_____

_____

Find 2 things **shorter** than your shoe.

_____

_____

Taller, shorter, thicker, thinner

Find someone who is **taller** than you.

_____

Find someone who is **shorter** than you.

_____

Find something **thicker** than your thumb.

_____

Find something **thinner** than your little finger.

_____

Length: language

Longer, shorter, taller

Match

Mark the thicker

Mark the thinner

Length: ordering

15

In your group who has

the longest ✏️ _____

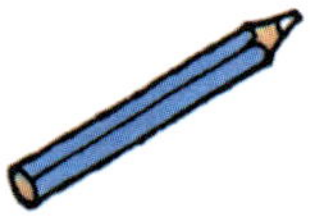

the shortest ✏️ ? _____

Colour the longest 🔴 
        the shortest 🔵

Length: ordering

16

In your group who is

tallest _____

shortest? _____

Colour the tallest

the shortest

Time stories

What time is it?

 o'clock

 o'clock

 o'clock

 o'clock

Match clocks which show the same time.

Problem solving

Time

Bus times

Colour the roads the bus takes.

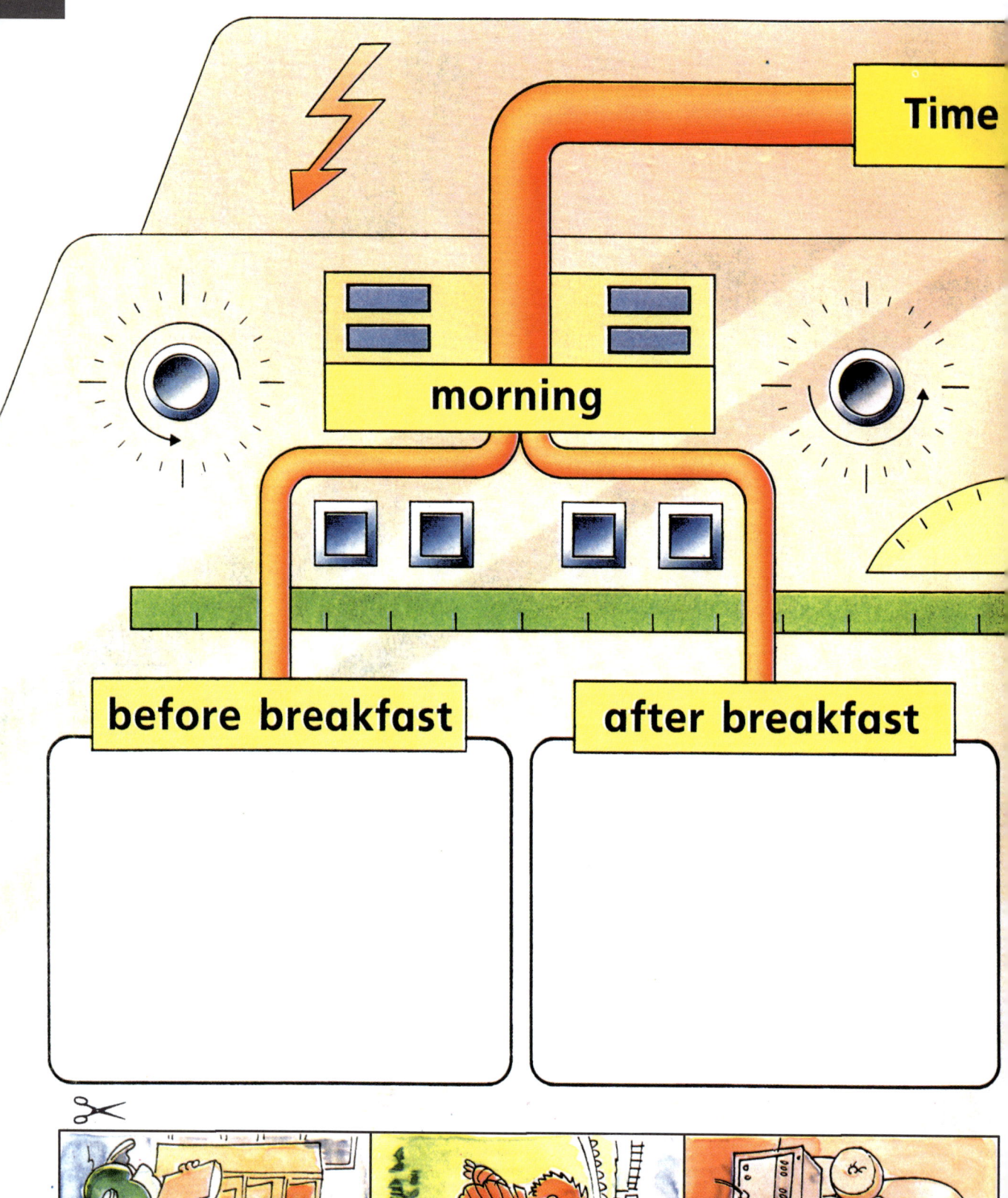

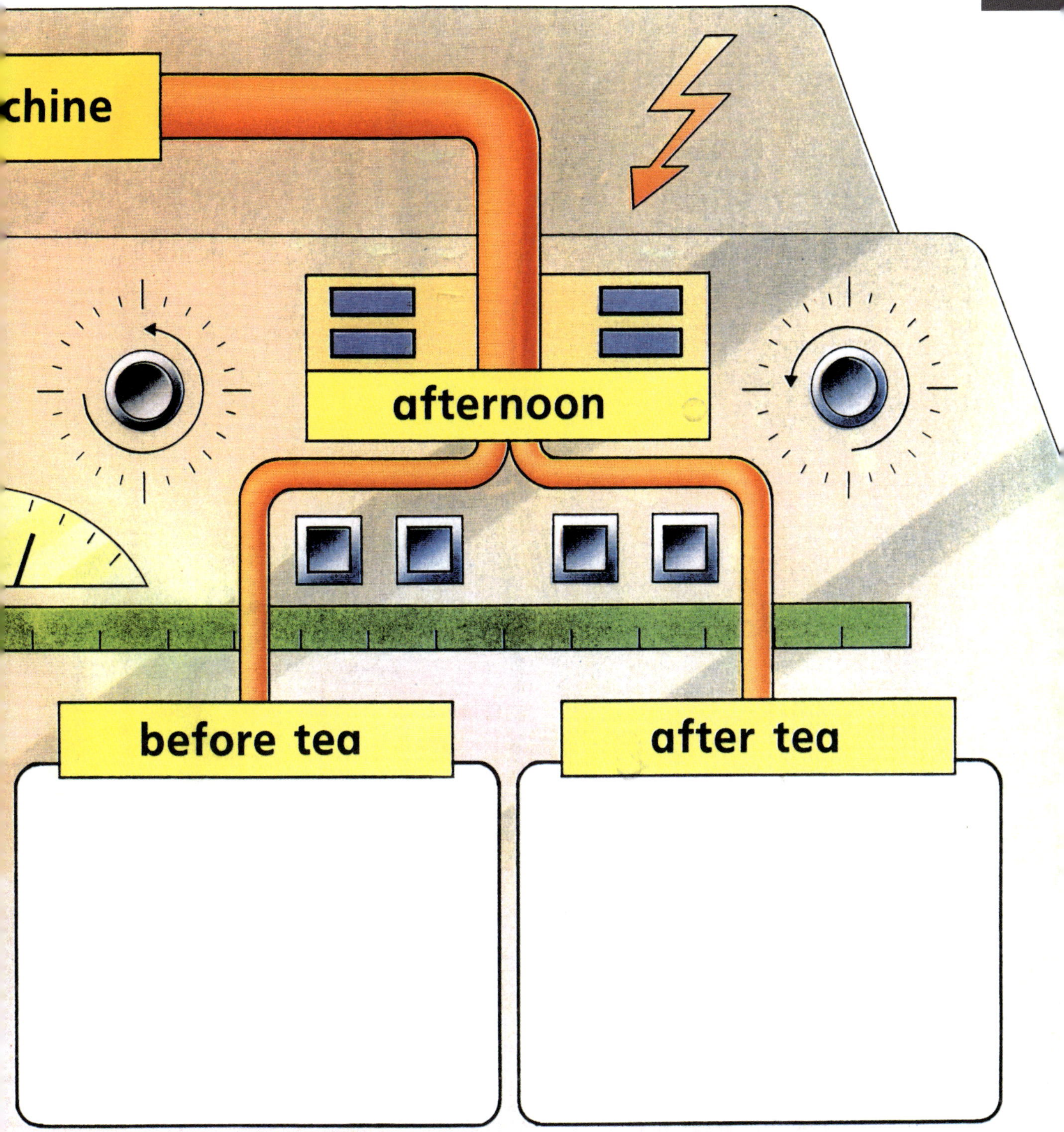

Time

22

chine

afternoon

before tea | after tea

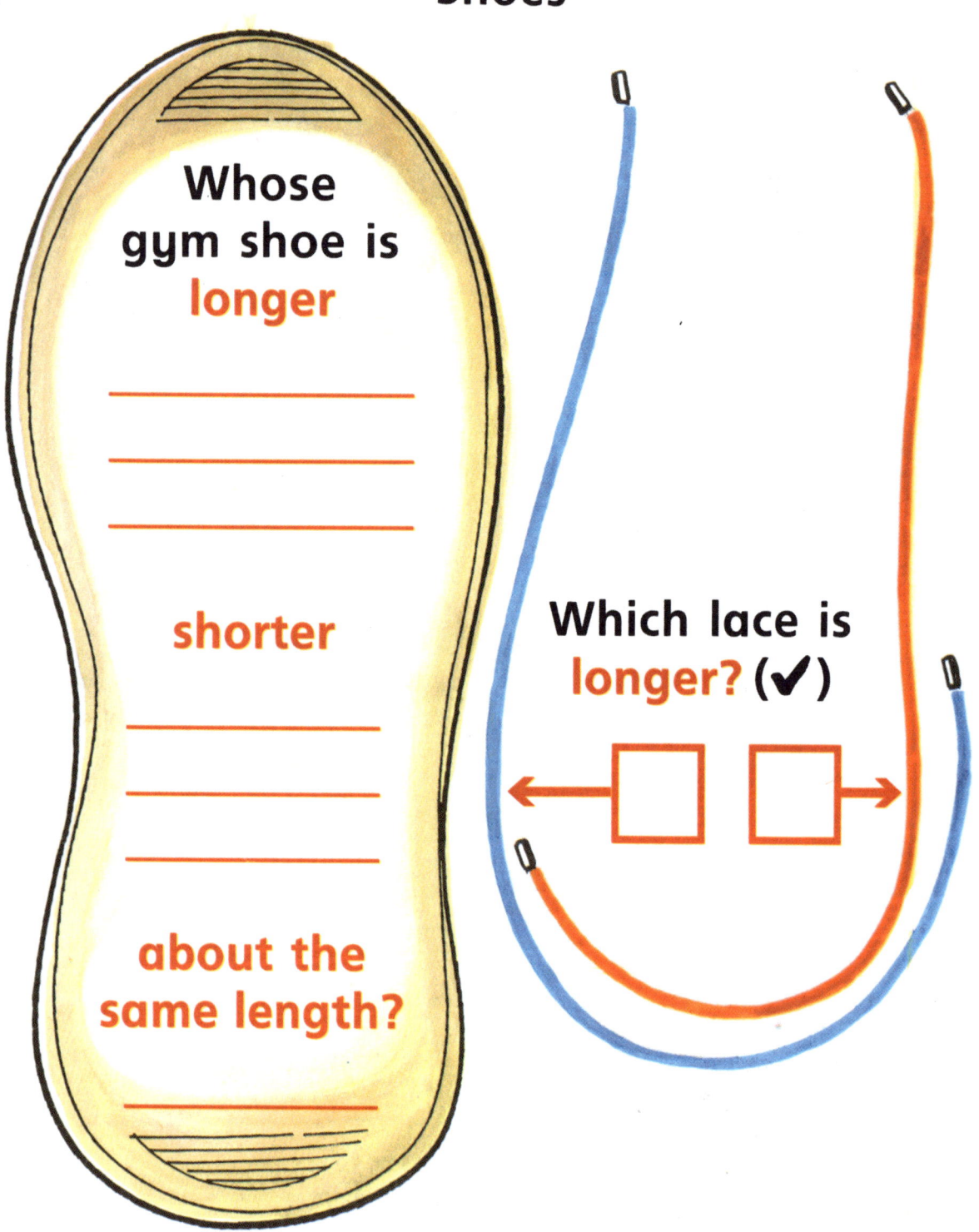

HEINEMANN MATHEMATICS 1

Name

MEASURE WORKBOOK

Revised

The Jungle

Length: language

2

How many:

thick trees ☐   thin trees ☐

thick snakes ☐   thin snakes ☐ ?

Time: language   **Problem solving**

Day or night?

day   night

Colour the sky.

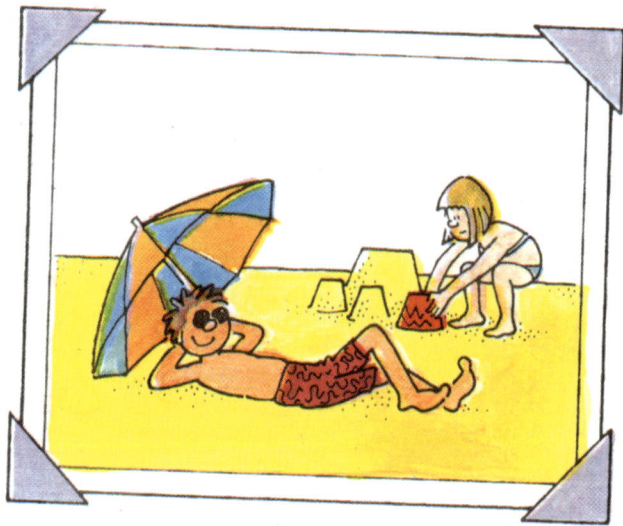 

Problem solving · Time: language

Morning or afternoon?

Colour the morning pictures.

waking up

going home

tea time

taking in the milk

Time: language **Problem solving**

What happened after?

Colour

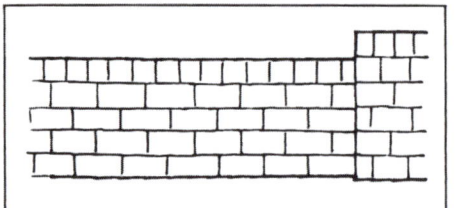

or

or

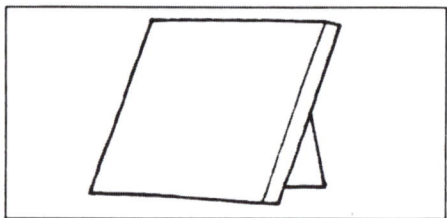

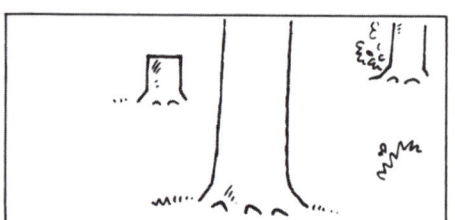

or

Problem solving | **Time: language**

What happened before?

Colour

or

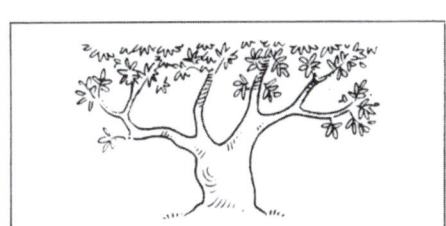

or

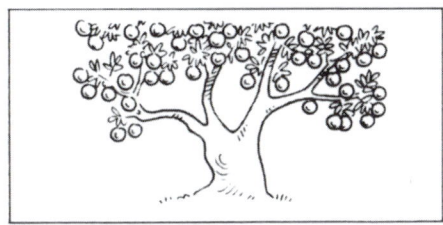

or

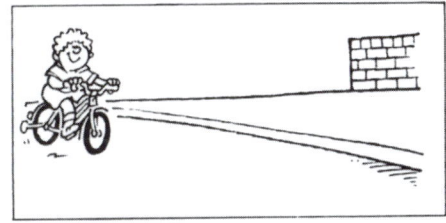

Heavier and lighter

Write [h] for heavier and [l] for lighter.

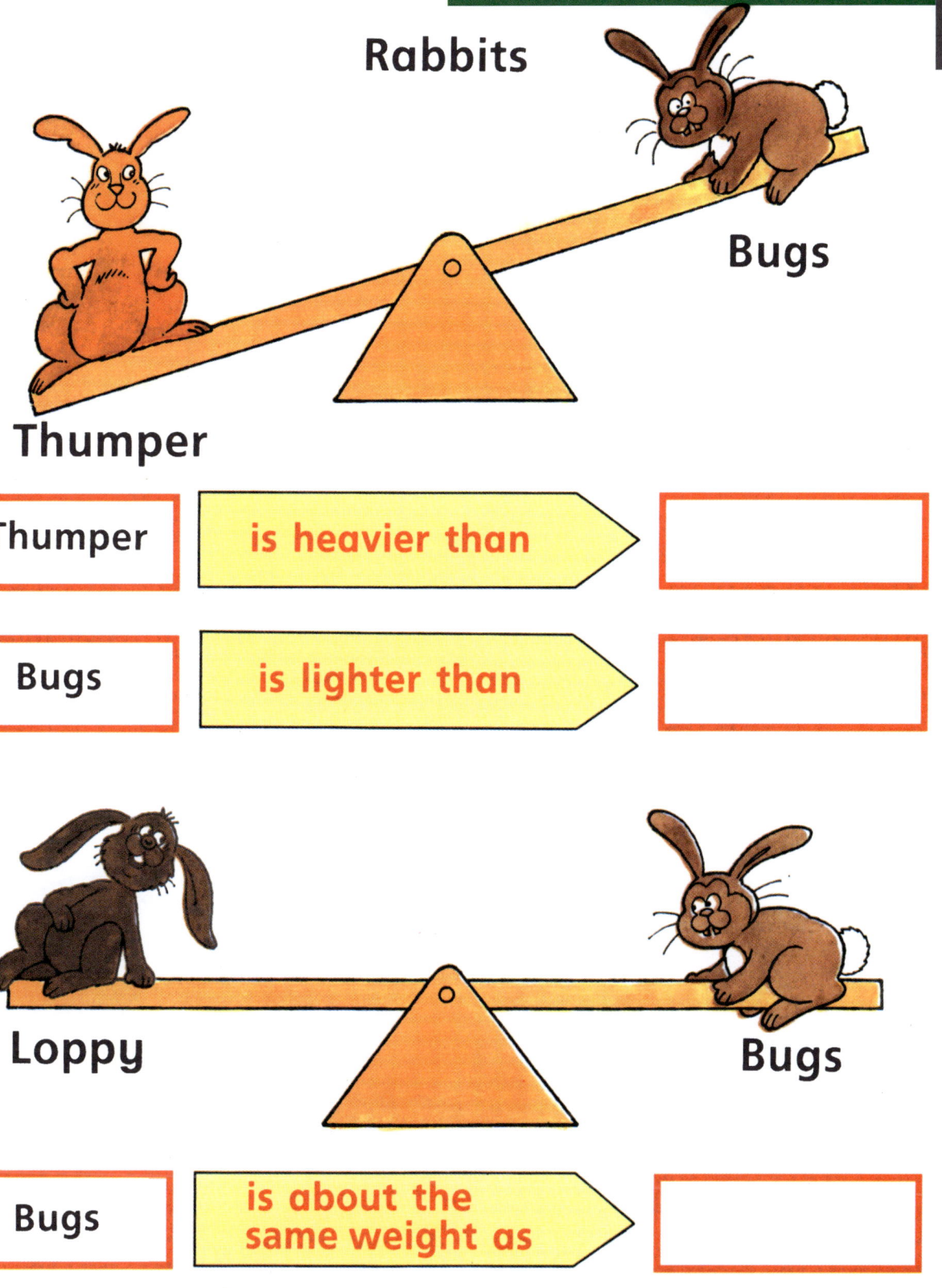

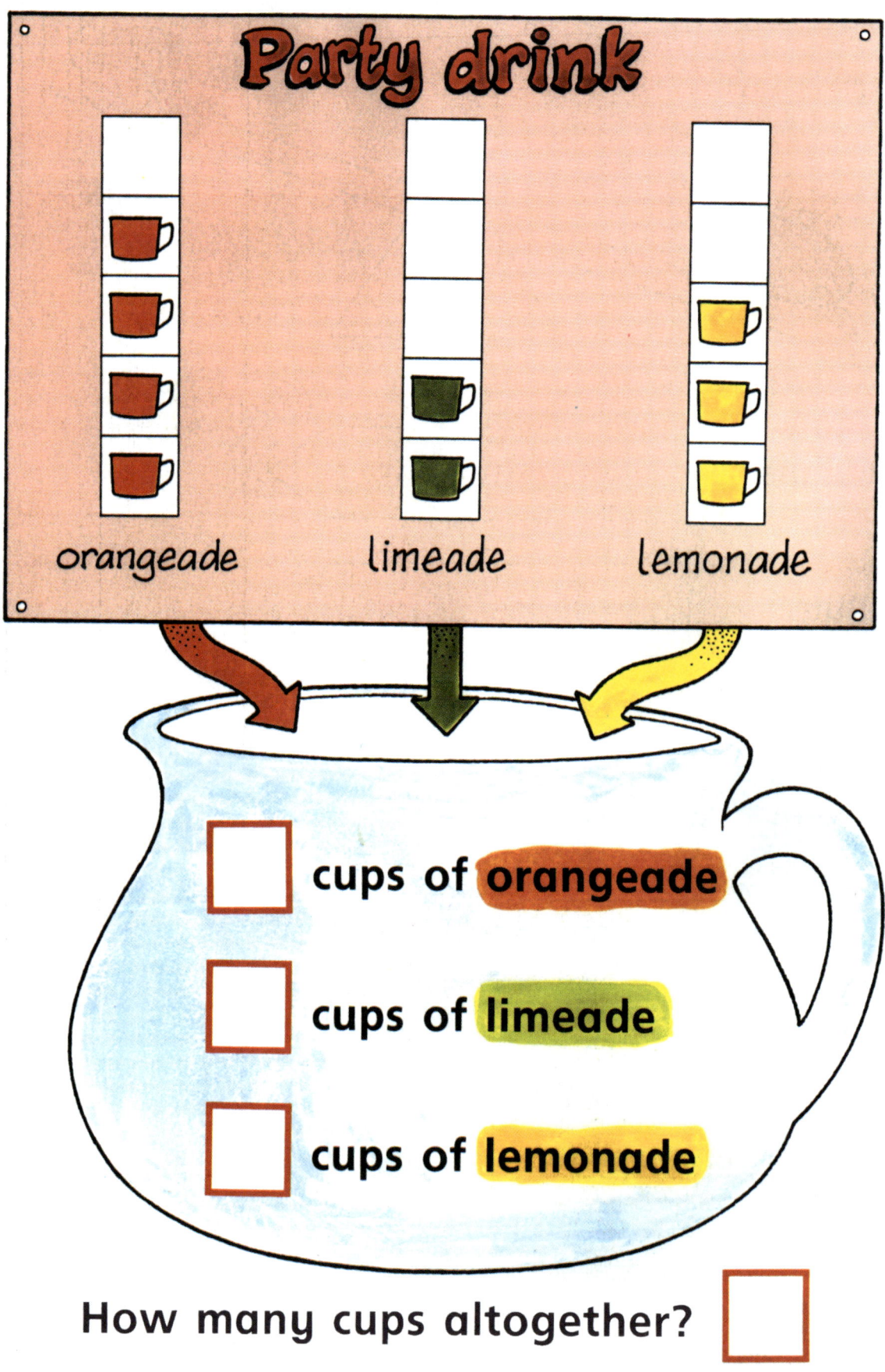

About how many cups does each fill?

Draw 🍵

Length: language

Longer and shorter

Find 2 things **longer** than your thumb.

_____

_____

Find 2 things **shorter** than your shoe.

_____

_____

Taller, shorter, thicker, thinner

Find someone who is **taller** than you.

_____

Find someone who is **shorter** than you.

_____

Find something **thicker** than your thumb.

_____

Find something **thinner** than your little finger.

_____

Length: language

14

Mark the **thicker**

Mark the **thinner**

Length: ordering

In your group who has

the longest ✏ _____

the shortest ✏ ? _____

Colour the longest 🔴
the shortest 🔵

Length: ordering

16

In your group who is

tallest _____

shortest? _____

Colour the tallest
the shortest

Time stories

Time: digital display

What time is it?

 o'clock

 o'clock

 o'clock

 o'clock

Match clocks which show the same time.

Problem solving Time

Bus times

Colour the roads the bus takes.

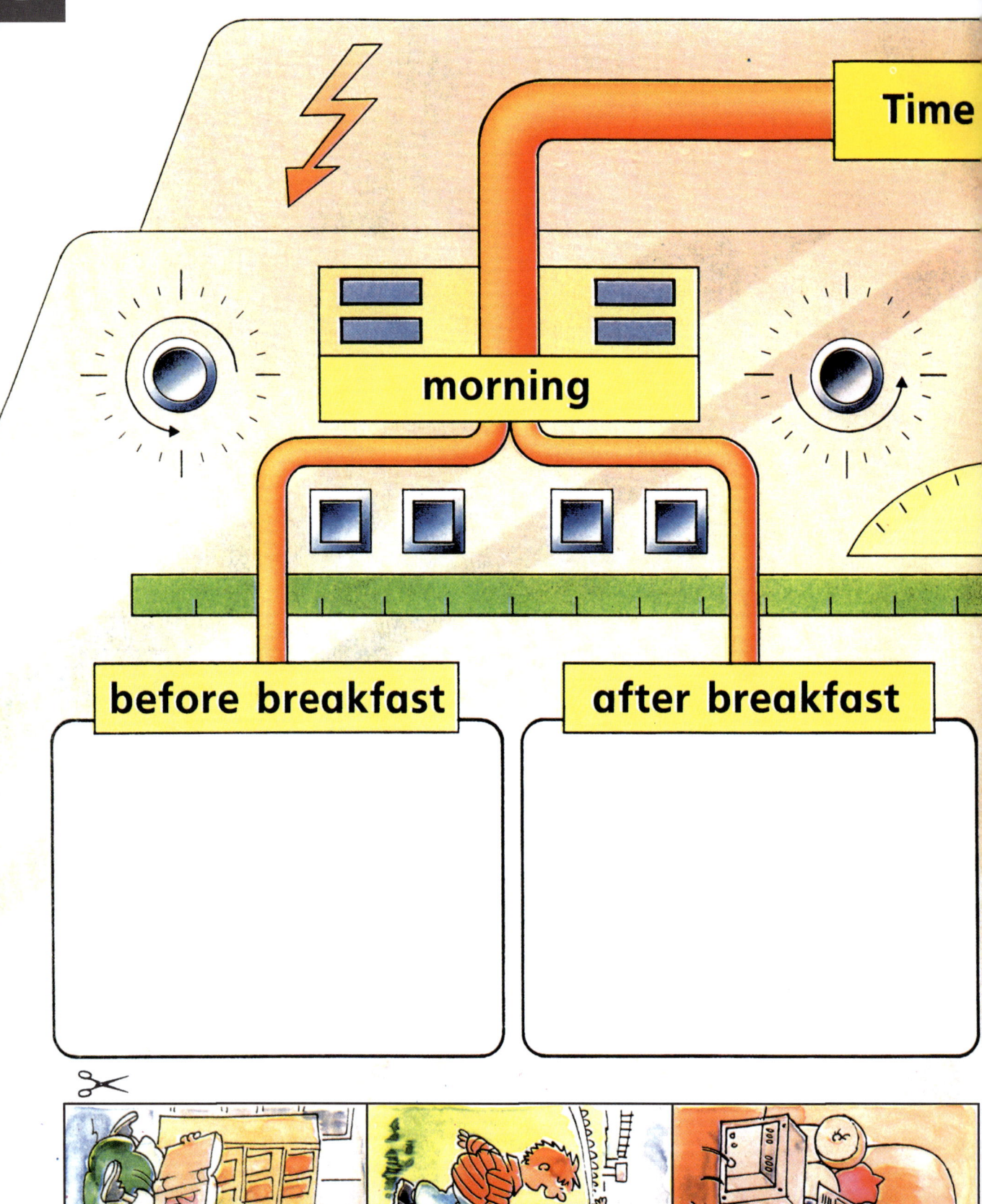

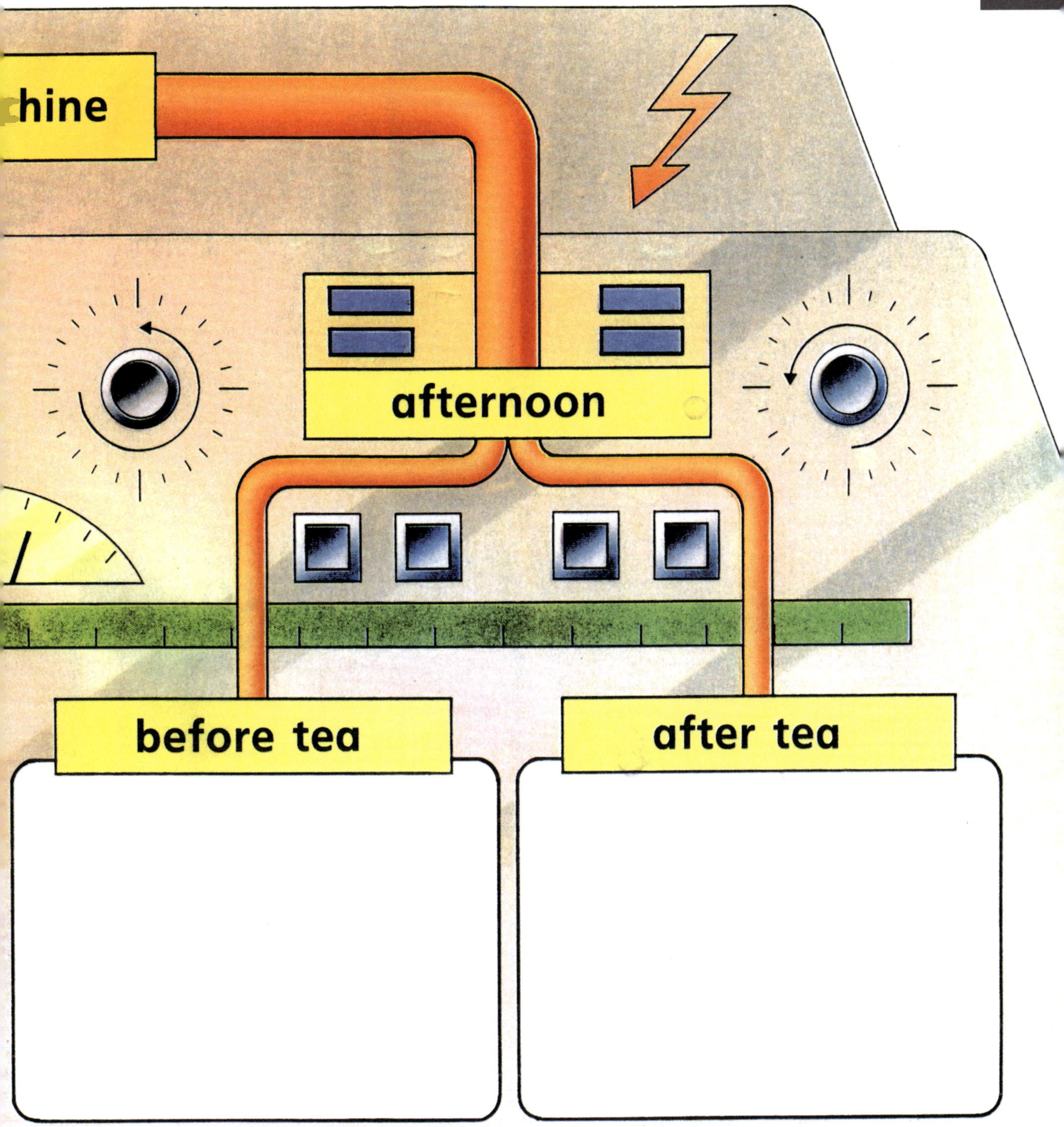

Time

22

hine

afternoon

before tea

after tea

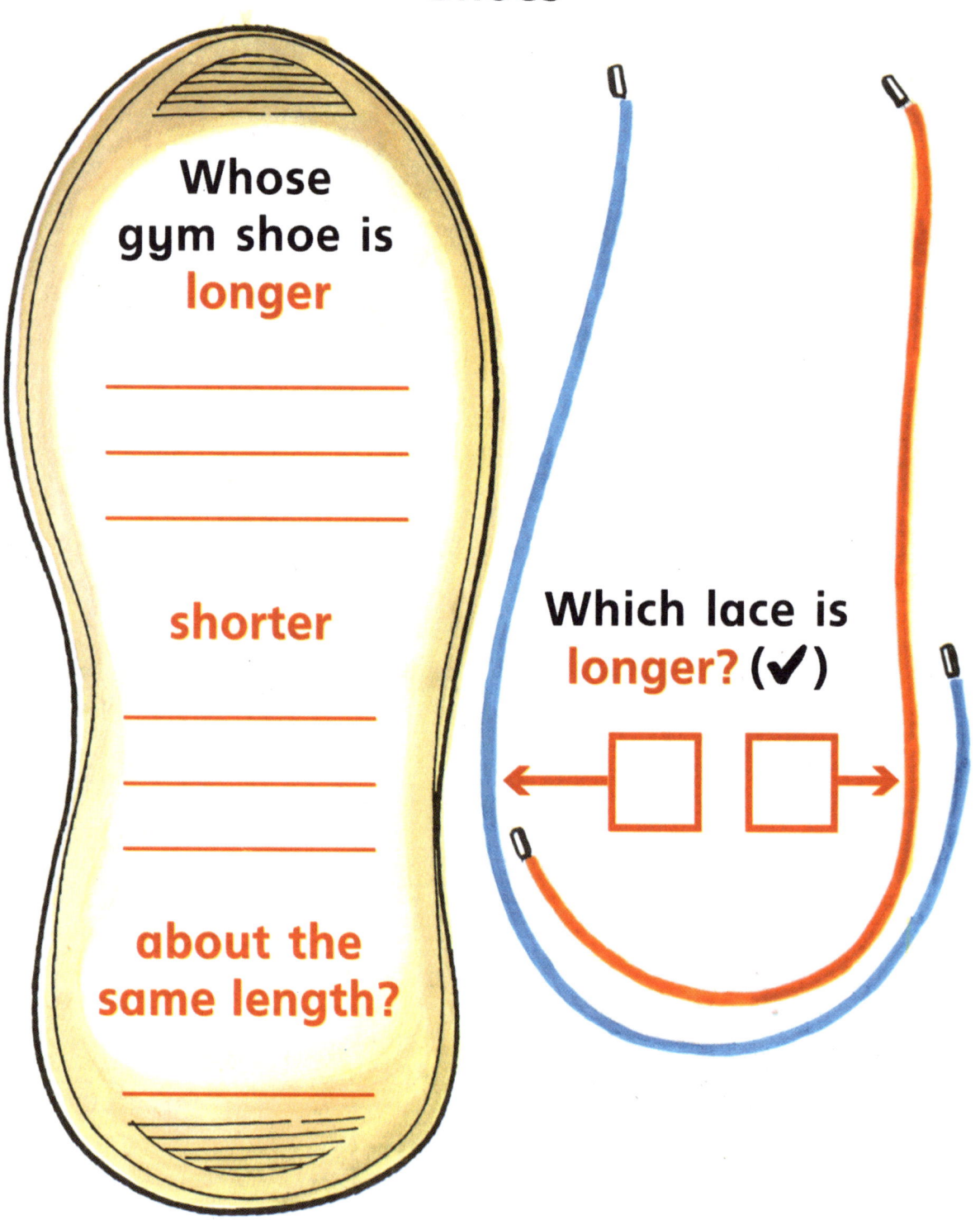

HEINEMANN MATHEMATICS 1

Name _____

MEASURE WORKBOOK

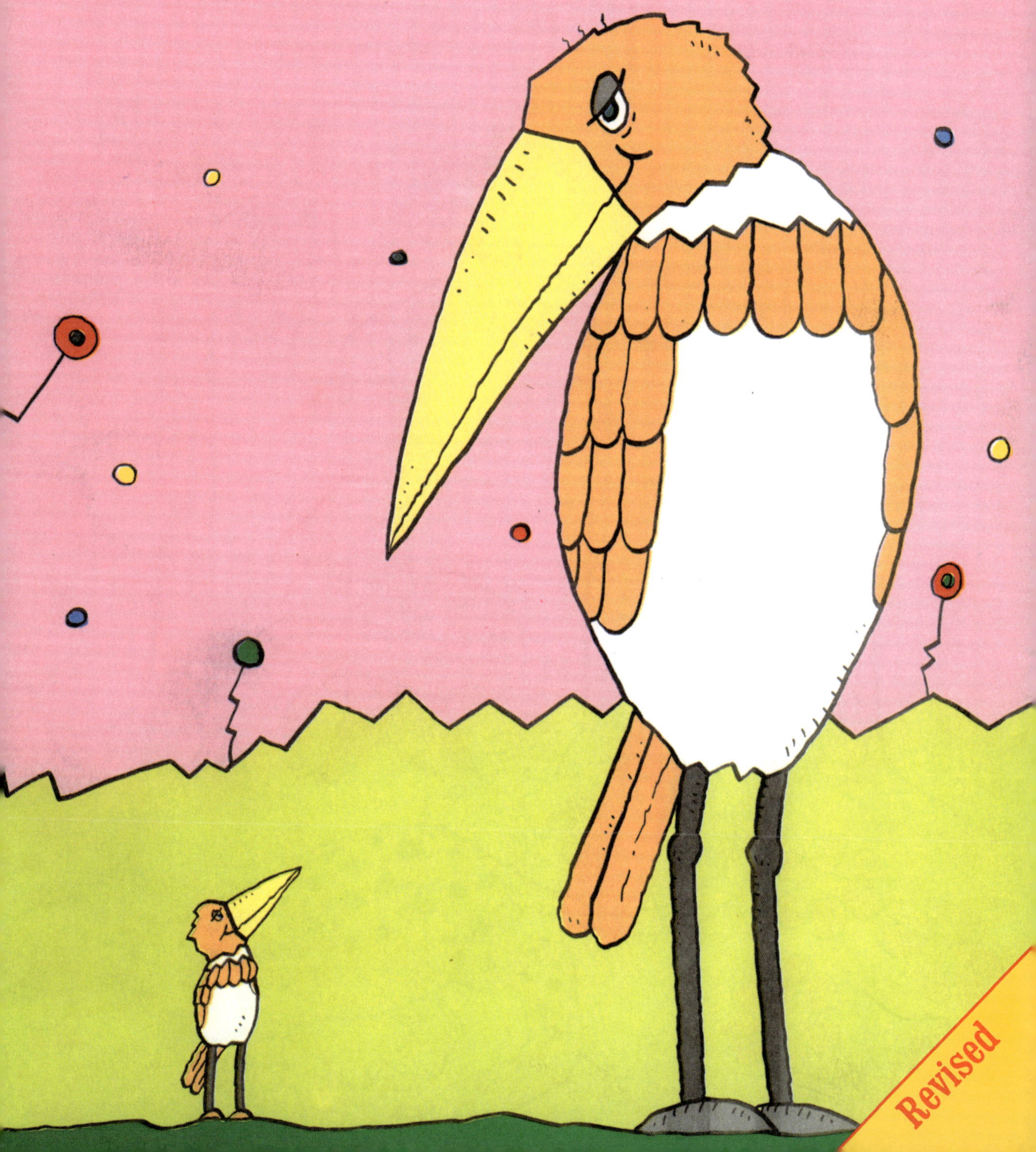

Revised

How many:

thick trees ☐ thin trees ☐

thick snakes ☐ thin snakes ☐ ?

Day or night?

day　　　　　　　　　　　　night

Colour the sky.

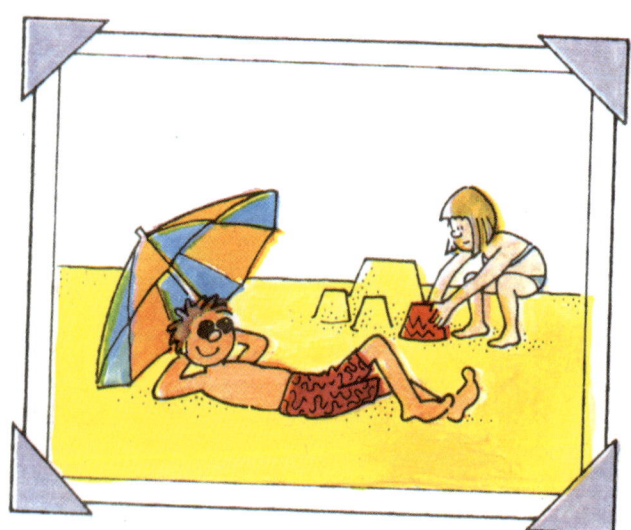 

Problem solving — Time: language

Morning or afternoon?

Colour the morning pictures.

waking up

going home

tea time

taking in the milk

5 Time: language Problem solving

What happened after?

Colour

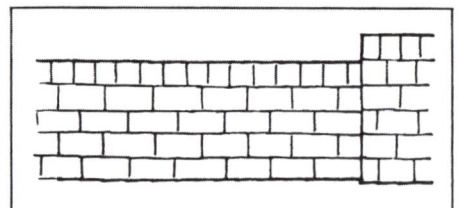

or

or

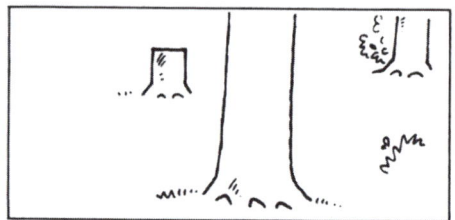

or

Problem solving   Time: language

What happened before?

Colour

or

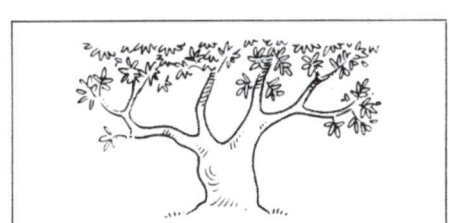
or
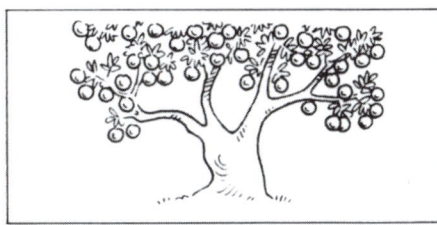

or
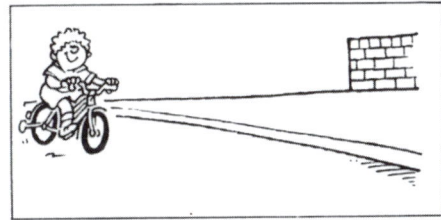

Heavier and lighter

Write **h** for heavier and **l** for lighter.

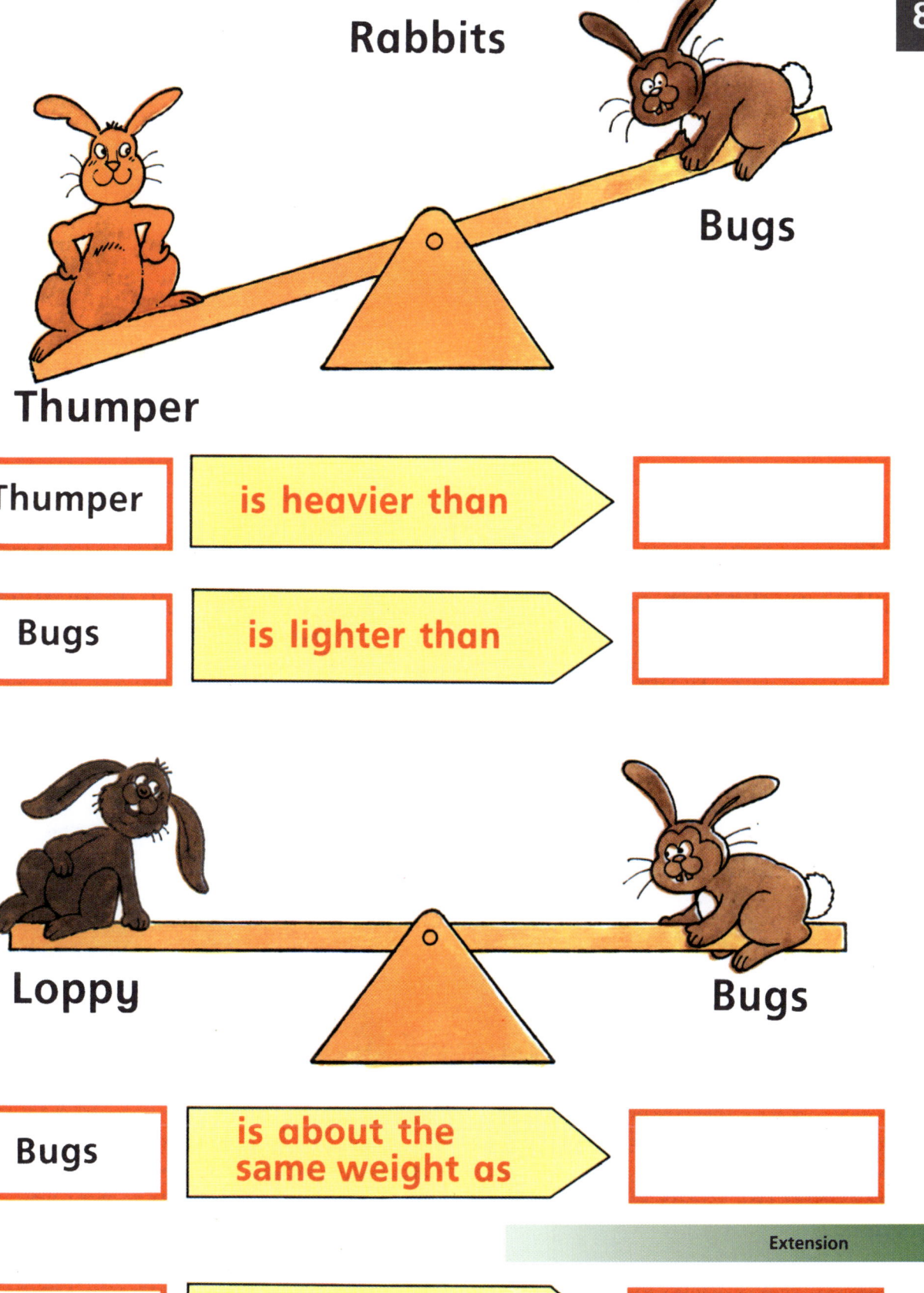

About how many cups does each fill?

Draw 🍵

Length: language

Longer and shorter

Find 2 things **longer** than your thumb.

_____

_____

Find 2 things **shorter** than your shoe.

_____

_____

Taller, shorter, thicker, thinner

Find someone who is taller than you.

Find someone who is shorter than you.

Find something thicker than your thumb.

Find something thinner than your little finger.

Mark the **thicker**

Mark the **thinner**

Length: ordering

In your group who has

the longest ✏️ _____

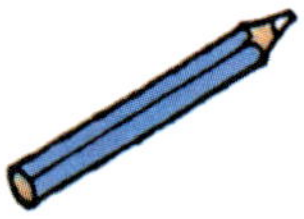

the shortest ✏️ ? _____

Colour the longest 🔴
the shortest 🔵

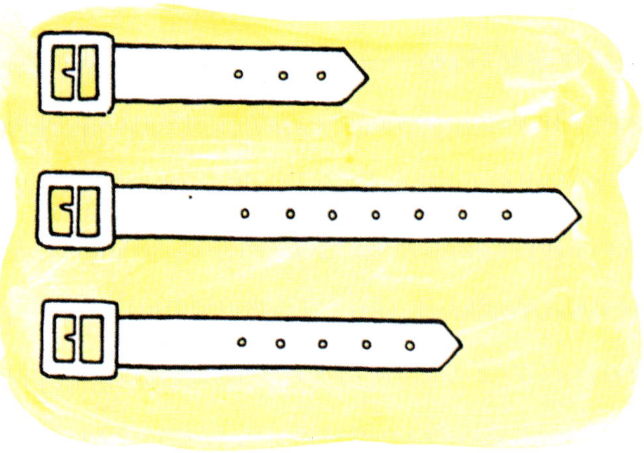

Length: ordering

16

In your group who is

tallest   _____

shortest? _____

Colour the tallest
the shortest

Time: o'clocks

What time is it?

o'clock   o'clock

o'clock   o'clock

o'clock   o'clock

o'clock   o'clock

Time stories

Time: digital display

What time is it?

 ☐ o'clock

 ☐ o'clock

 ☐ o'clock

 ☐ o'clock

Match clocks which show the same time.

Problem solving — Time

Bus times

Colour the roads the bus takes.

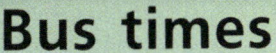

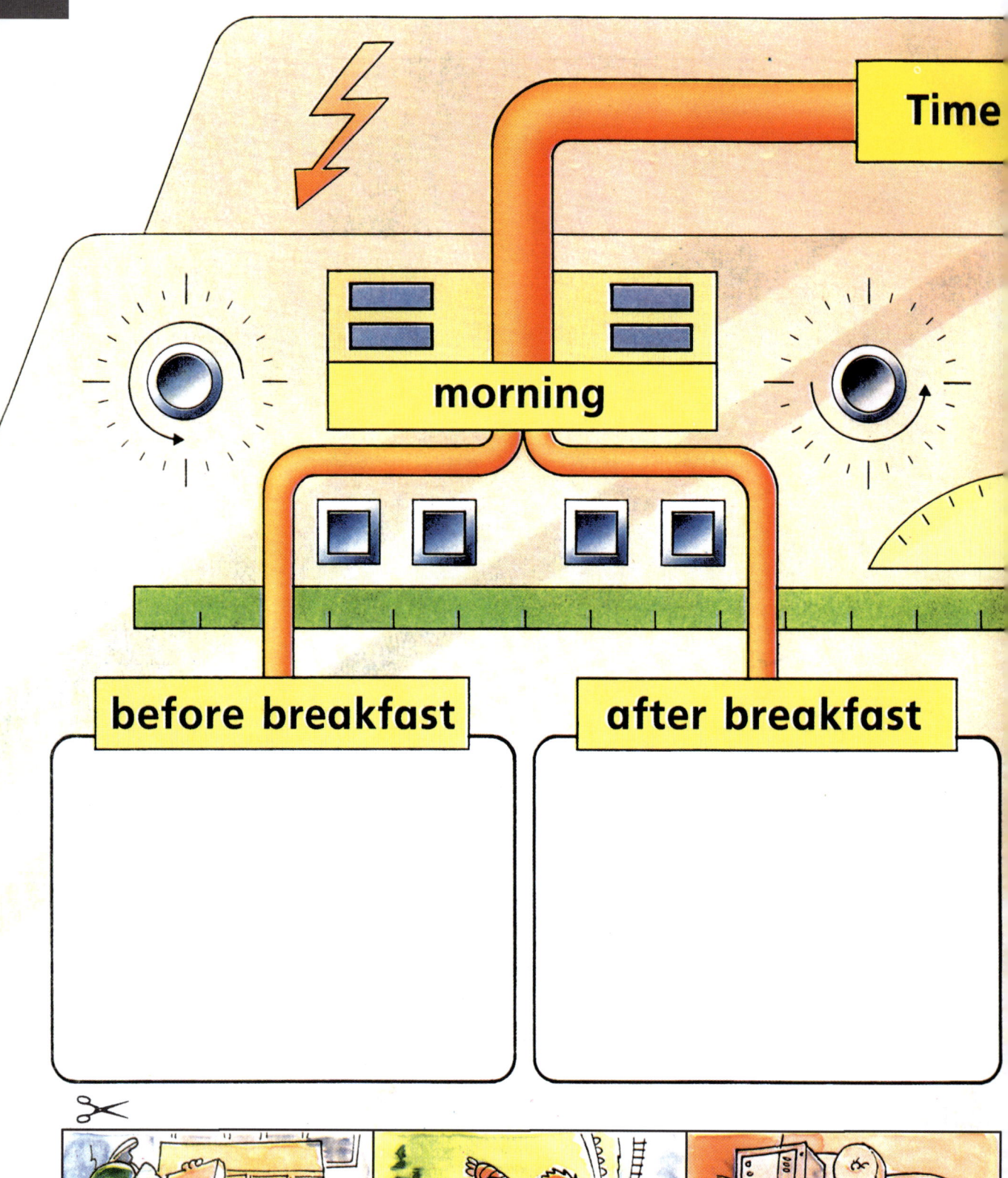

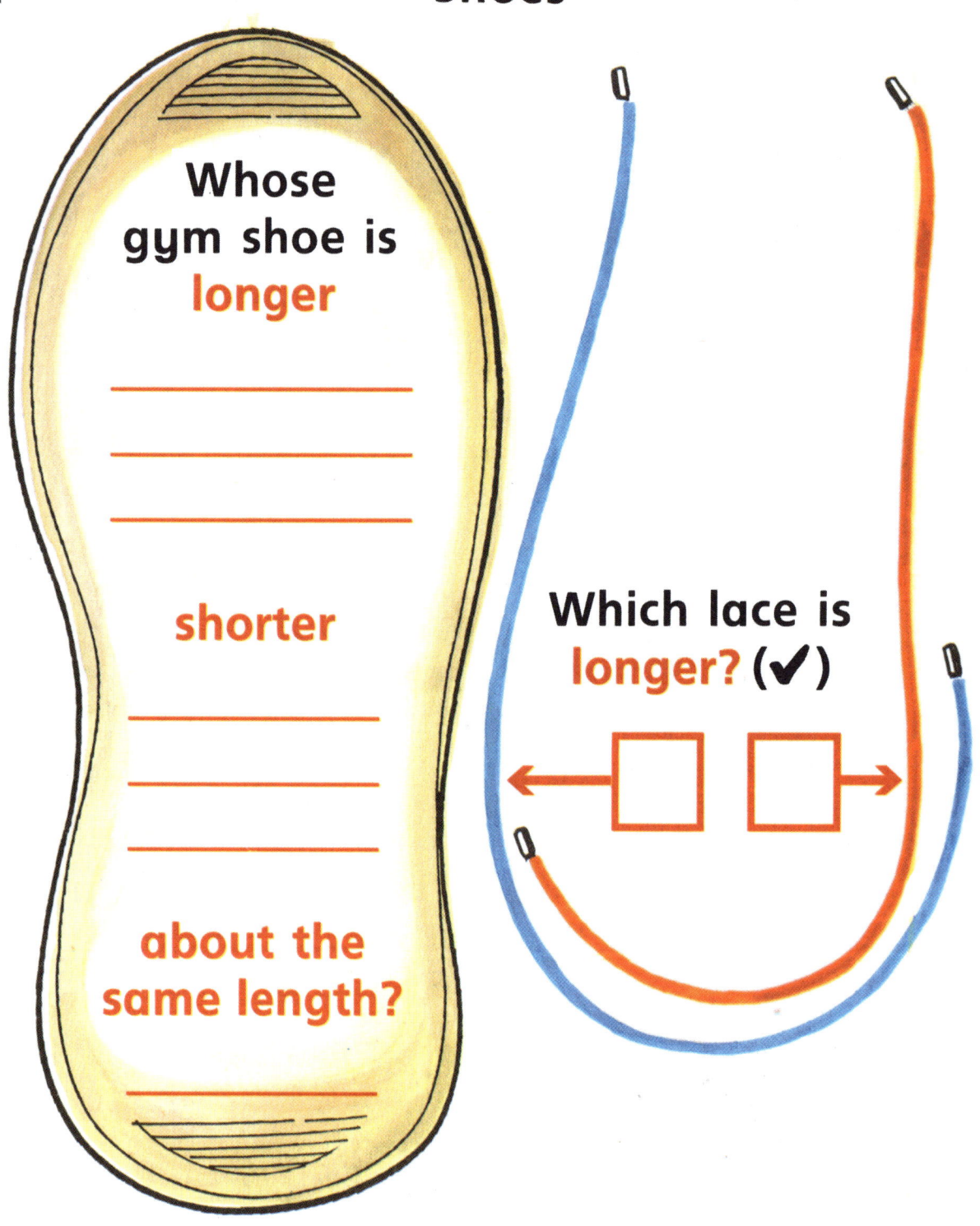

SPMG

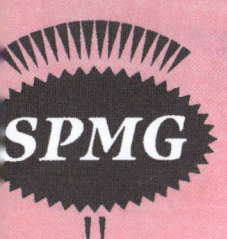

HEINEMANN MATHEMATICS 1

Name ______________________

MEASURE WORKBOOK

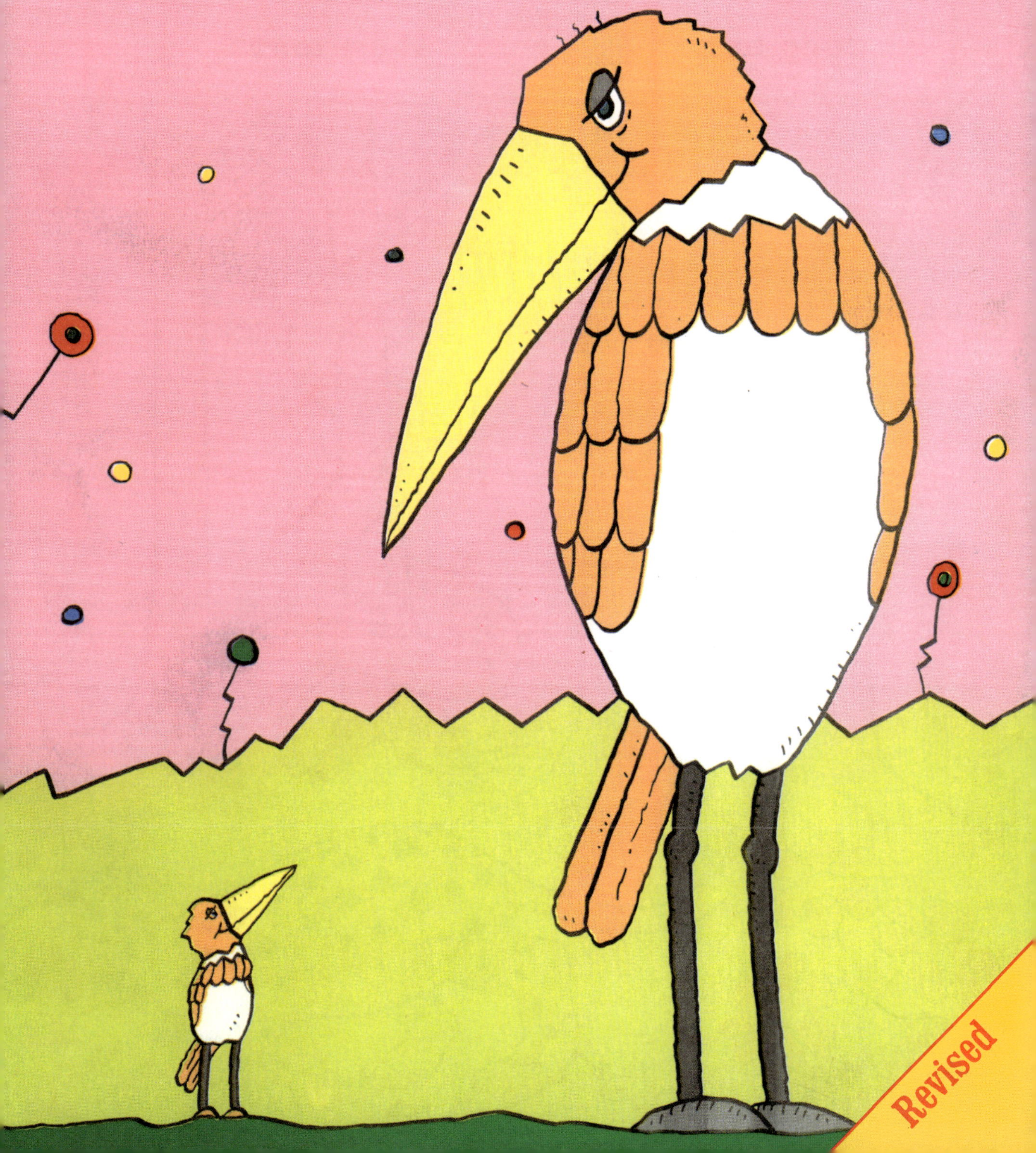

Revised

The Jungle

Length: language

2

How many:

thick trees ☐   thin trees ☐

thick snakes ☐   thin snakes ☐ ?

Time: language   **Problem solving**

Day or night?

day   night

Colour the sky.

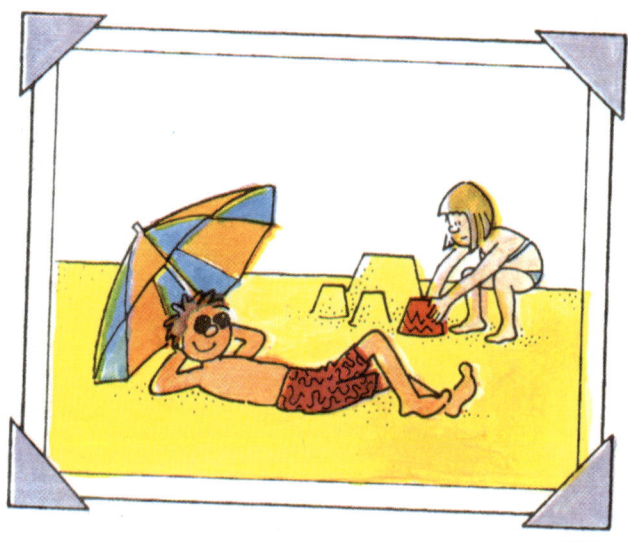 

Problem solving　　　　　　Time: language

Morning or afternoon?

Colour the morning pictures.

waking up

going home

tea time

taking in the milk

Time: language | Problem solving

5

What happened after?

Colour

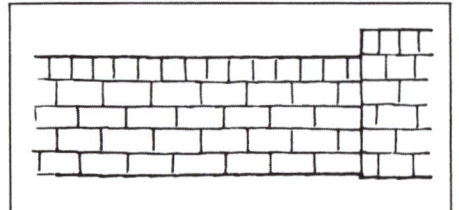

or

or

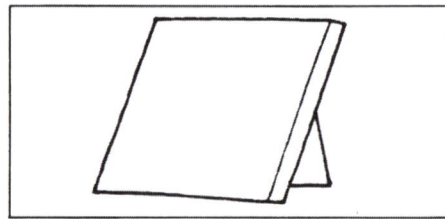

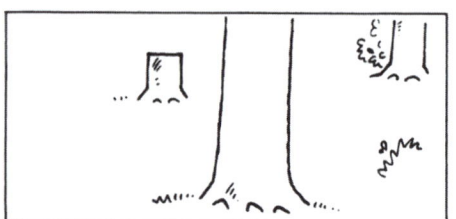

or

Problem solving | **Time: language**

What happened before?

Colour

or

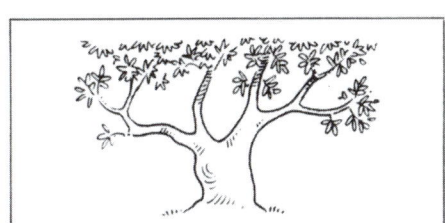

or

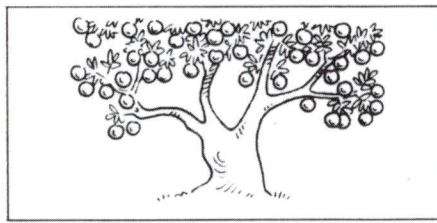

or

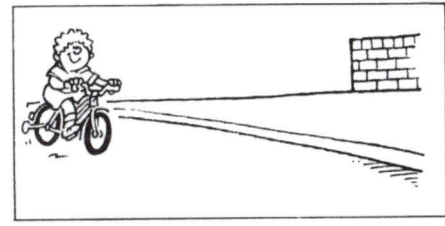

Heavier and lighter

Write **h** for heavier and **l** for lighter.

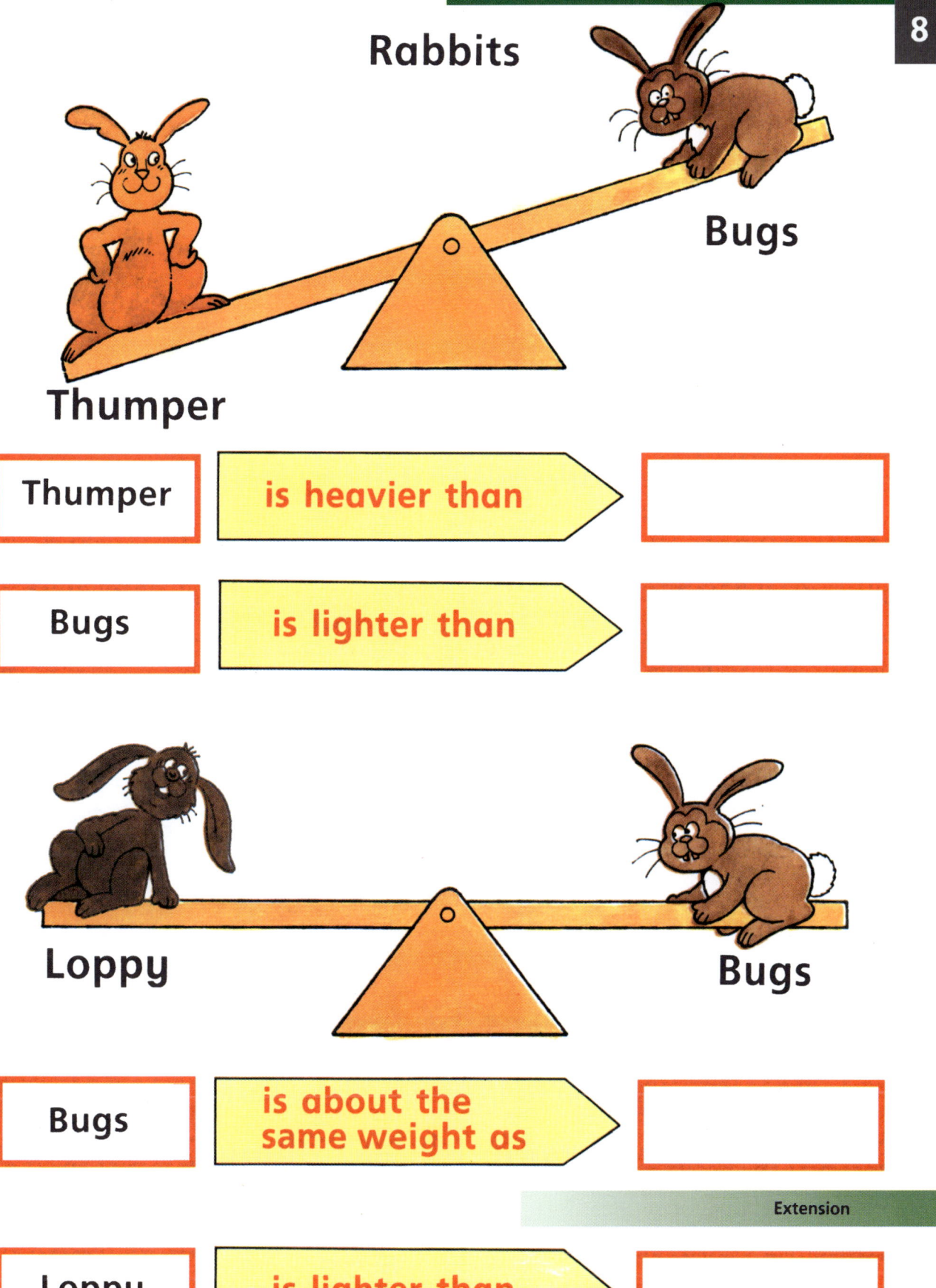

About how many cups does each fill?

Draw 🍵

Length: language

Longer and shorter

Find 2 things **longer** than your thumb.

_____

_____

Find 2 things **shorter** than your shoe.

_____

_____

Length: language

Taller, shorter, thicker, thinner

Find someone who is taller than you.

_____

Find someone who is shorter than you.

_____

Find something thicker than your thumb.

_____

Find something thinner than your little finger.

_____

Longer, shorter, taller
Match

Length: language

Mark the **thicker**

Mark the **thinner**

Length: ordering

In your group who has

the longest ✏️ _____

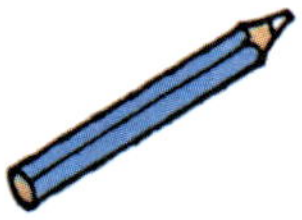

the shortest ✏️ ? _____

Colour the longest 🔴
the shortest 🔵

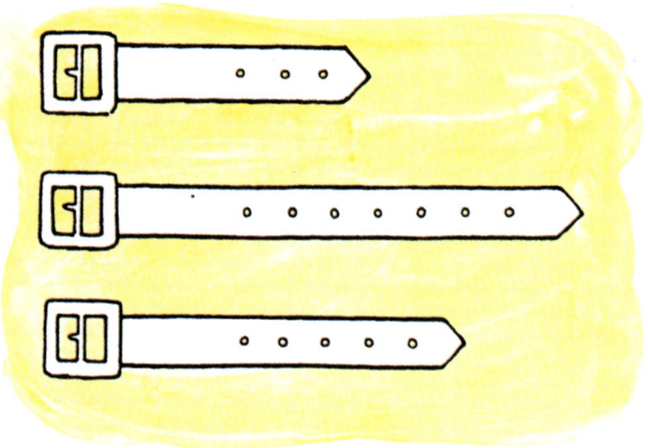

In your group who is

tallest _____

shortest? _____

Colour the tallest
the shortest

What time is it?

Time stories

What time is it?

 ☐ o'clock

 ☐ o'clock

 ☐ o'clock

 ☐ o'clock

Match clocks which show the same time.

Bus times

Colour the roads the bus takes.

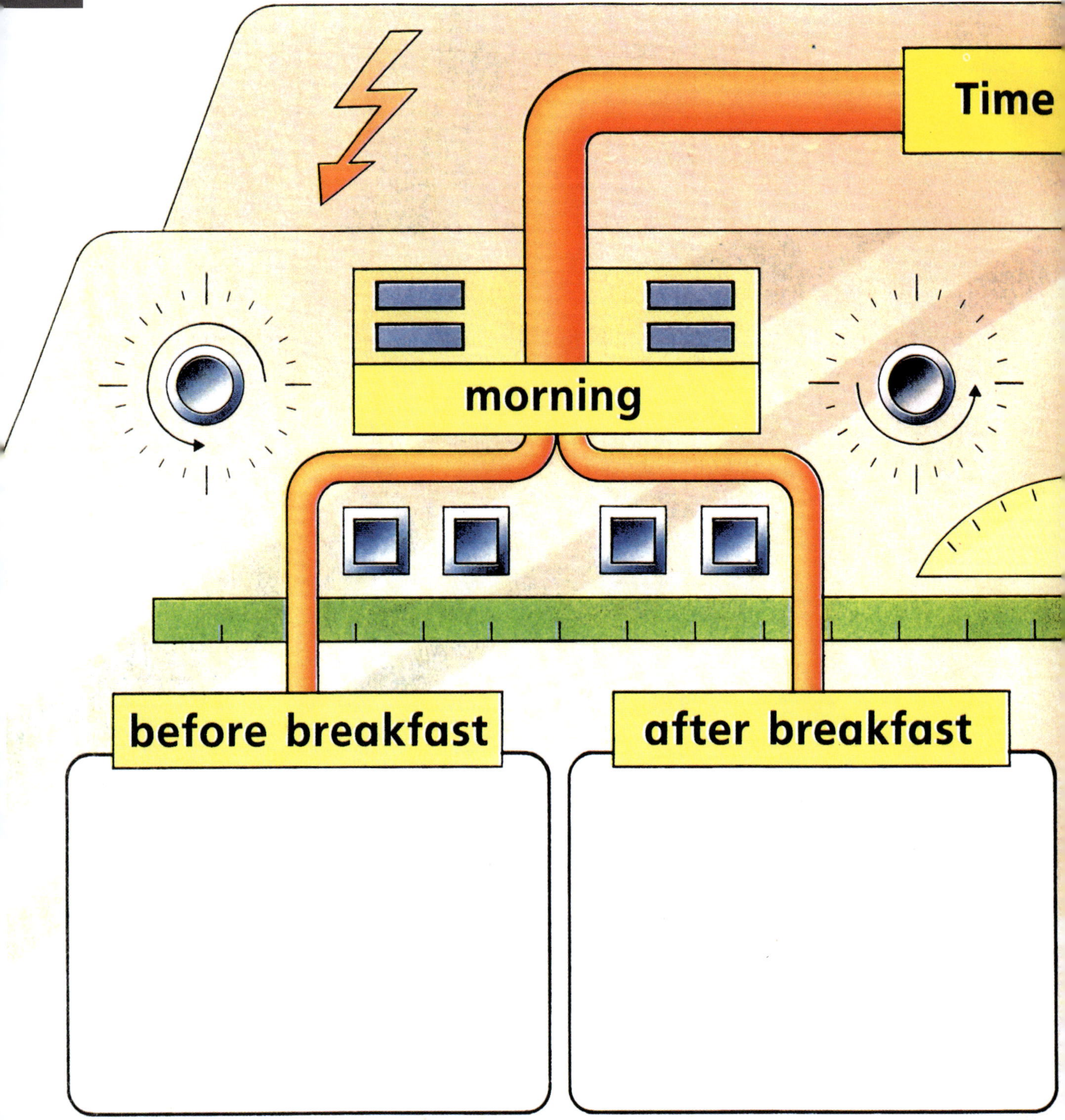

Time

Problem solving

Time

morning

before breakfast | **after breakfast**

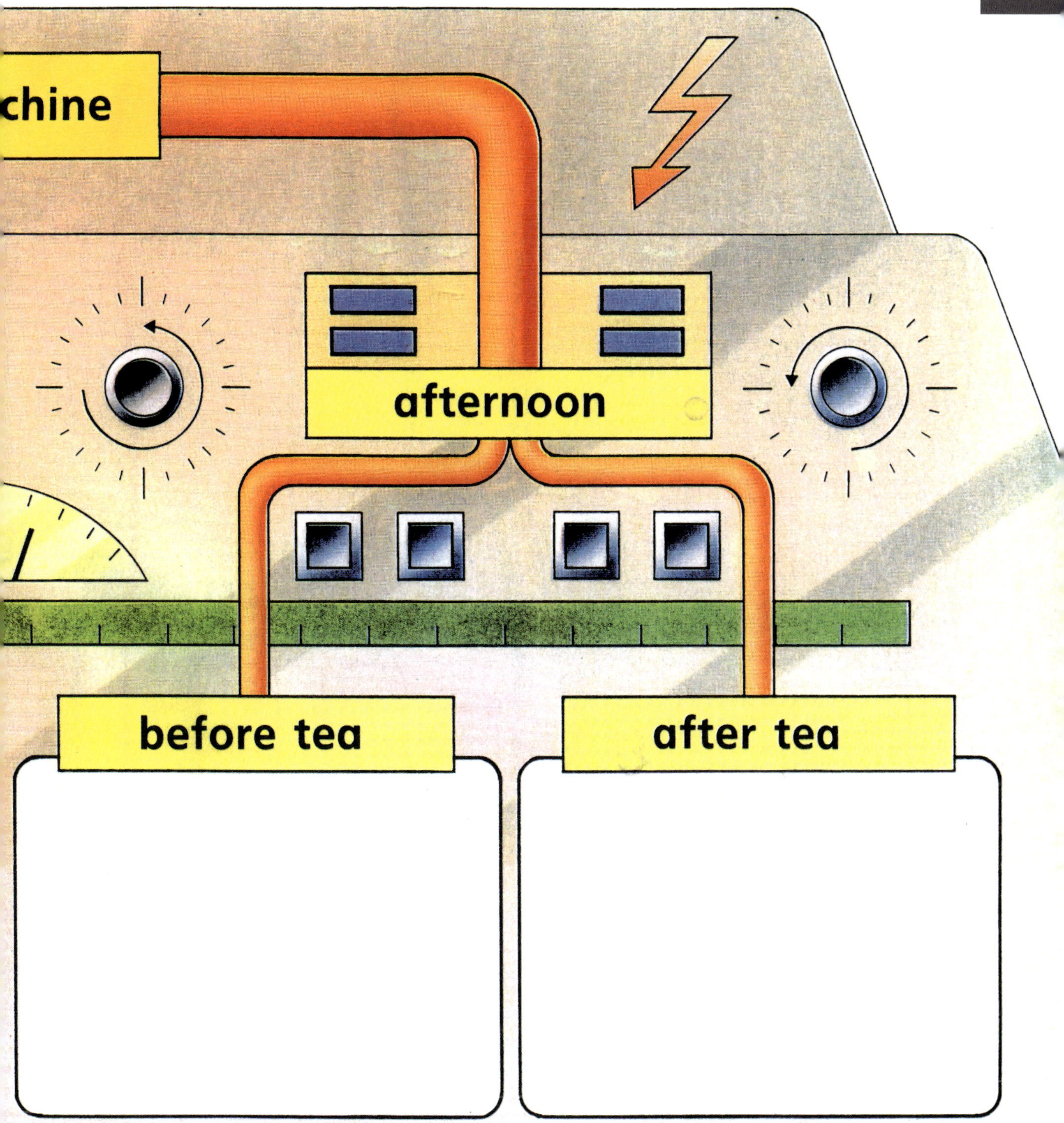

chine

afternoon

before tea

after tea

Length: comparison   Group work

Shoes

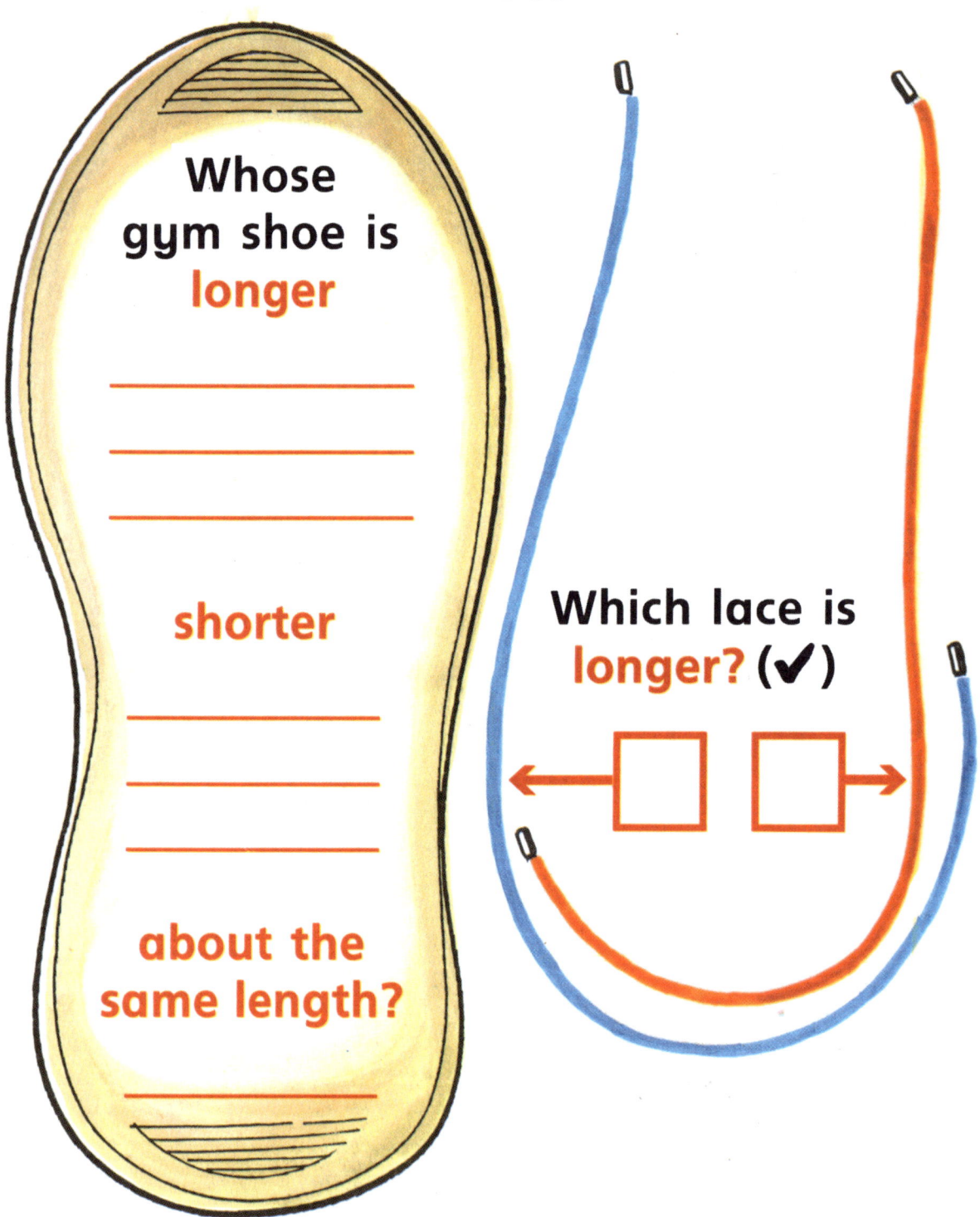

SPMG

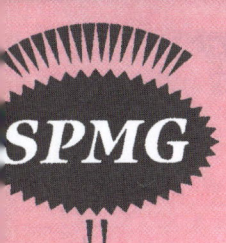

HEINEMANN MATHEMATICS 1

Name

MEASURE WORKBOOK

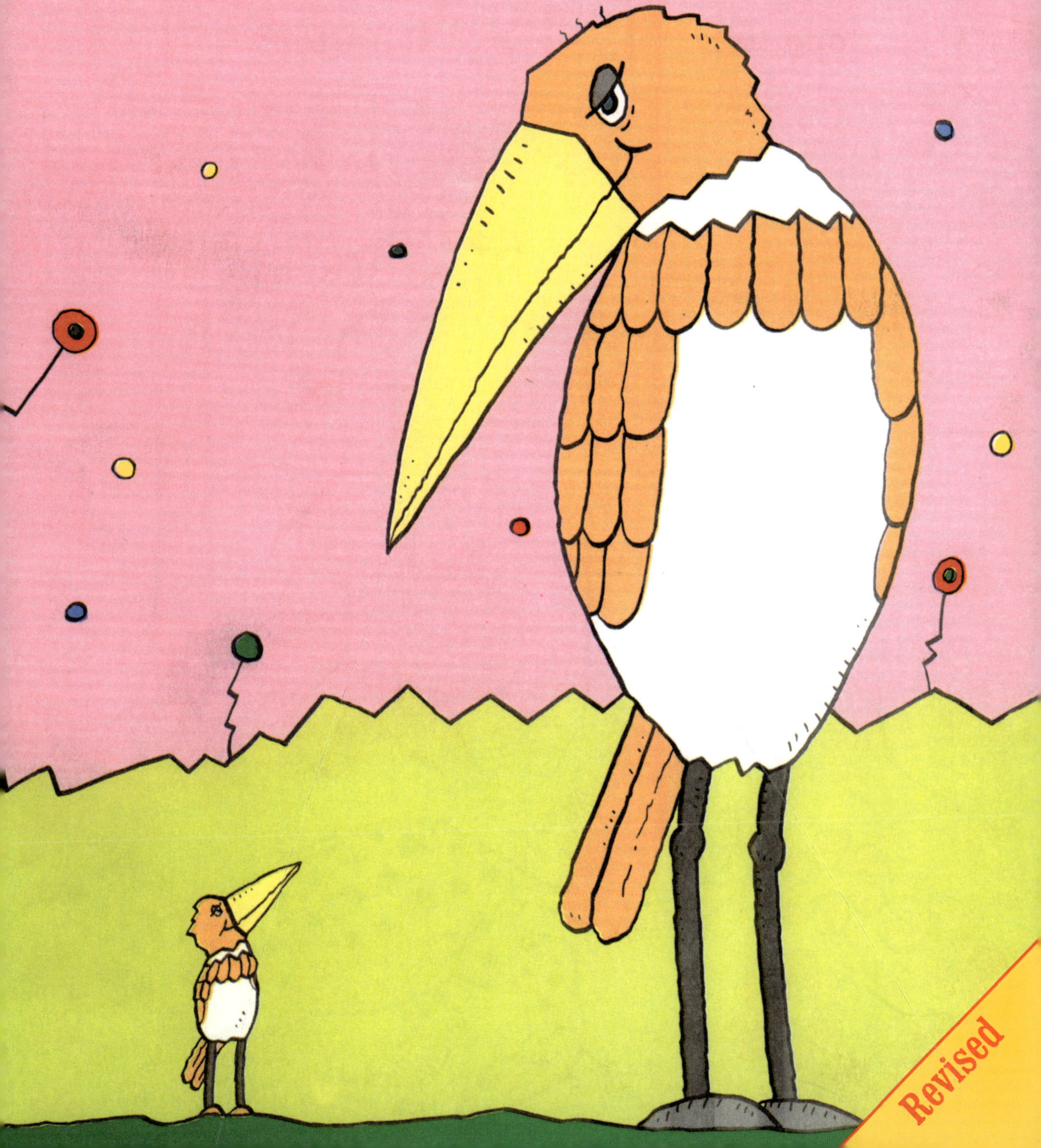

Revised

The Jungle

Length: language

2

How many:

thick trees ☐   thin trees ☐

thick snakes ☐   thin snakes ☐ ?

Day or night?

day　　　　　　　　　　　　　night

Colour the sky.

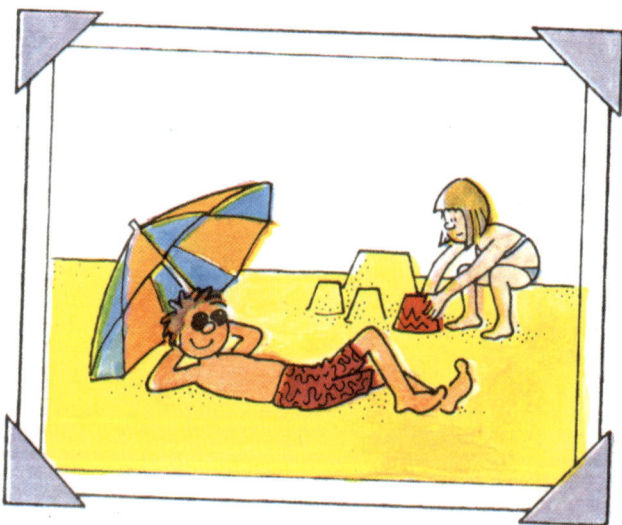 

Problem solving — **Time: language**

Morning or afternoon?

Colour the morning pictures.

waking up

going home

tea time

taking in the milk

Time: language   **Problem solving**

What happened after?

Colour

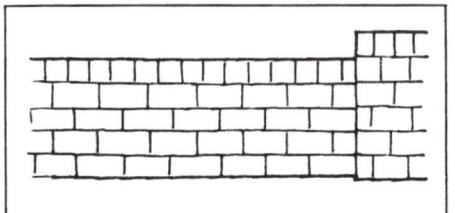

or

or

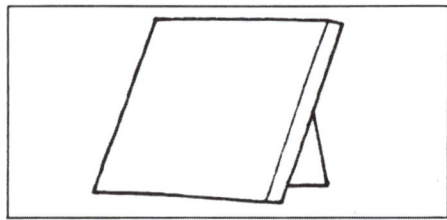

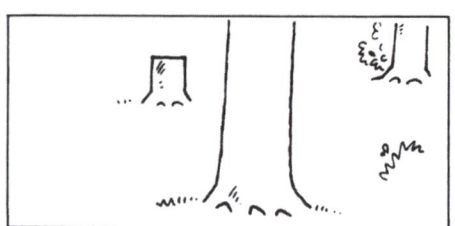

or

Problem solving   Time: language

What happened before?

Colour

or

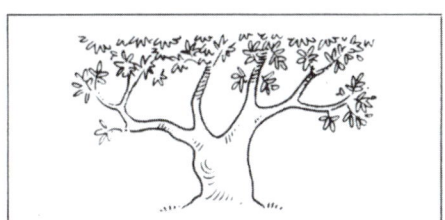
or
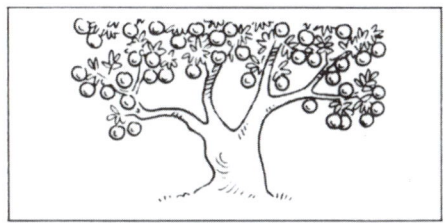

or
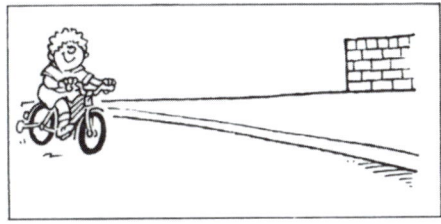

Heavier and lighter

Write [h] for heavier and [l] for lighter.

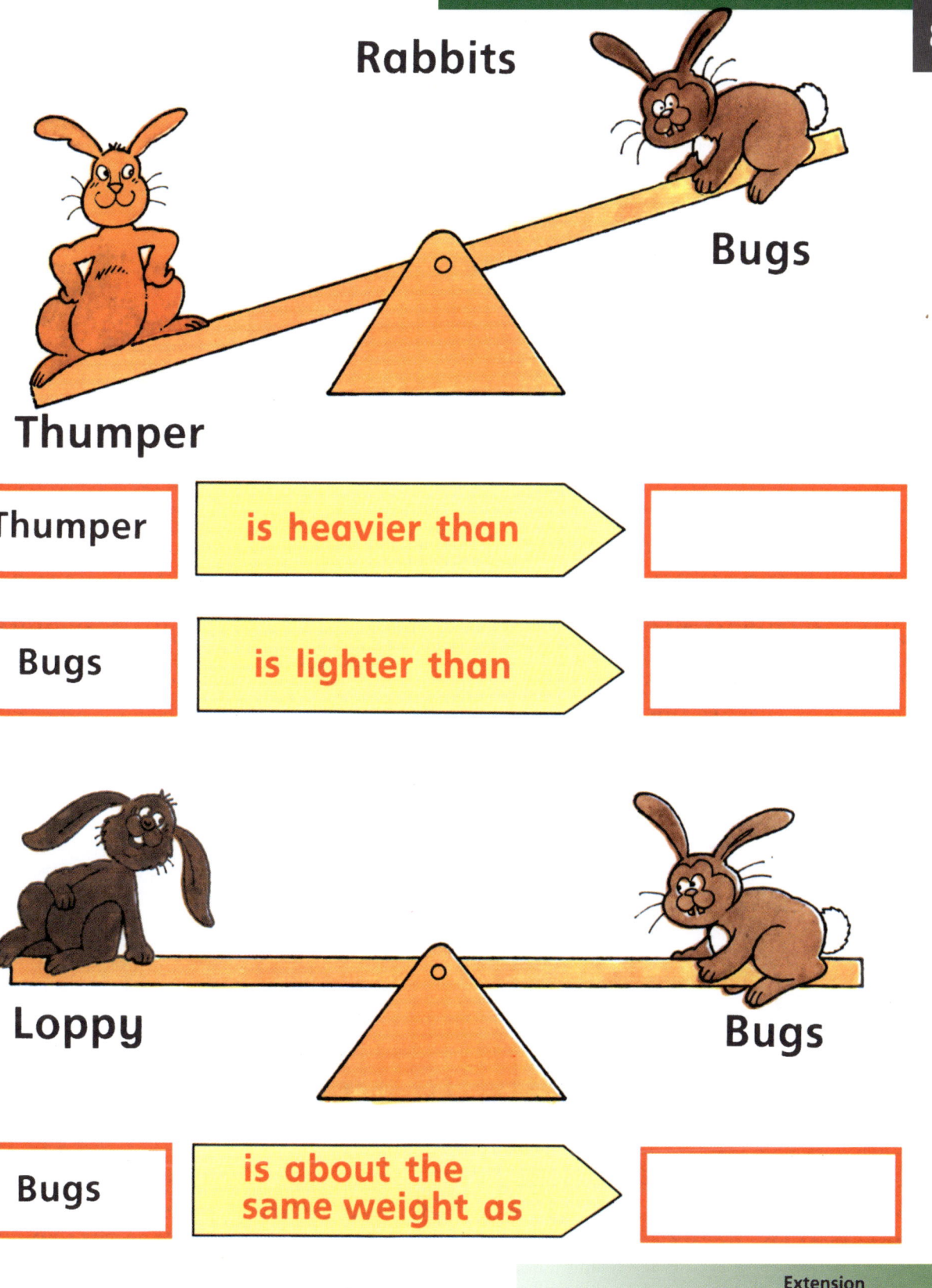

About how many cups does each fill?

Draw 🍵

Longer and shorter

Find 2 things **longer** than your thumb.

_____

_____

Find 2 things **shorter** than your shoe.

_____

_____

Length: language

Taller, shorter, thicker, thinner

Find someone who is taller than you.

_____

Find someone who is shorter than you.

_____

Find something thicker than your thumb.

_____

Find something thinner than your little finger.

_____

12

Longer, shorter, taller
Match

Length: language

Mark the thicker

Mark the thinner

Length: ordering

15

In your group who has

the longest ✏️ _____

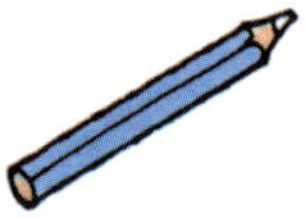

the shortest ✏️ ? _____

Colour the longest 🔴 
the shortest 🔵

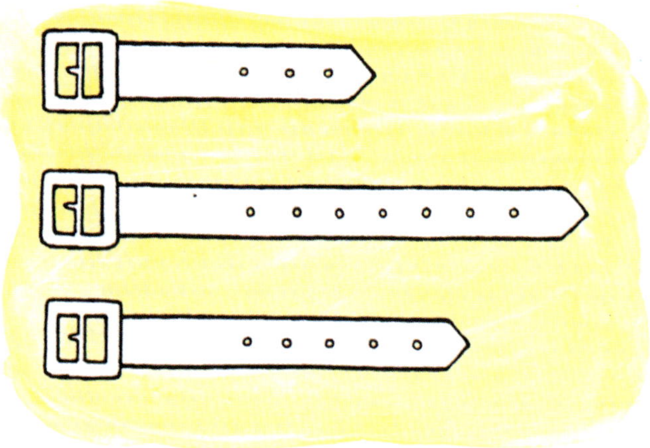

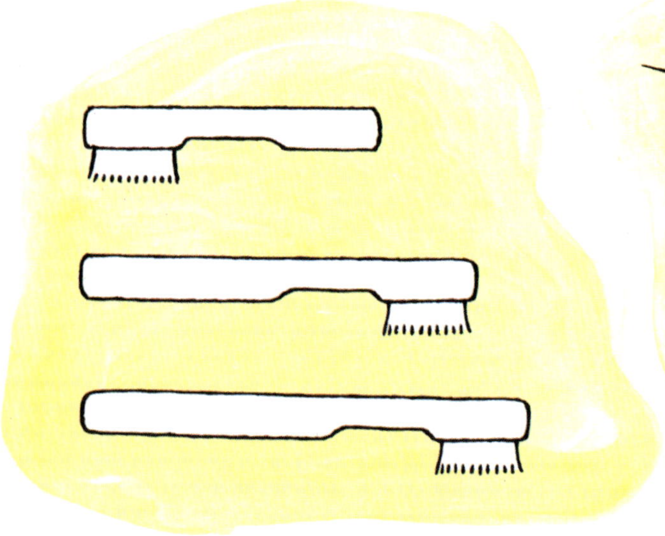

Length: ordering

In your group who is

tallest _____

shortest? _____

Colour the tallest
the shortest

Time: o'clocks

Time stories

Time: digital display

What time is it?

 o'clock

 o'clock

 o'clock

 o'clock

Match clocks which show the same time.

Problem solving — Time

Bus times

Colour the roads the bus takes.

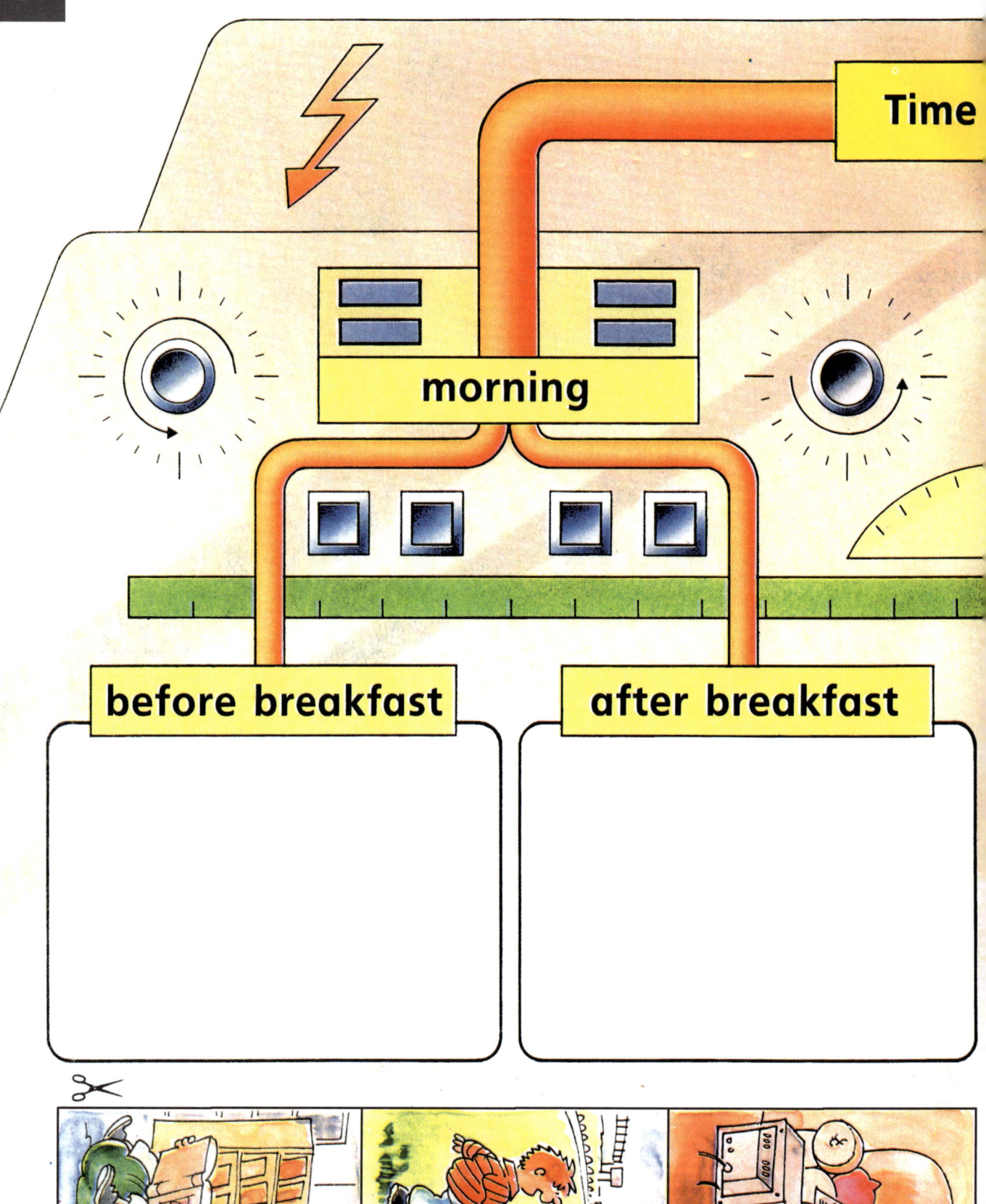

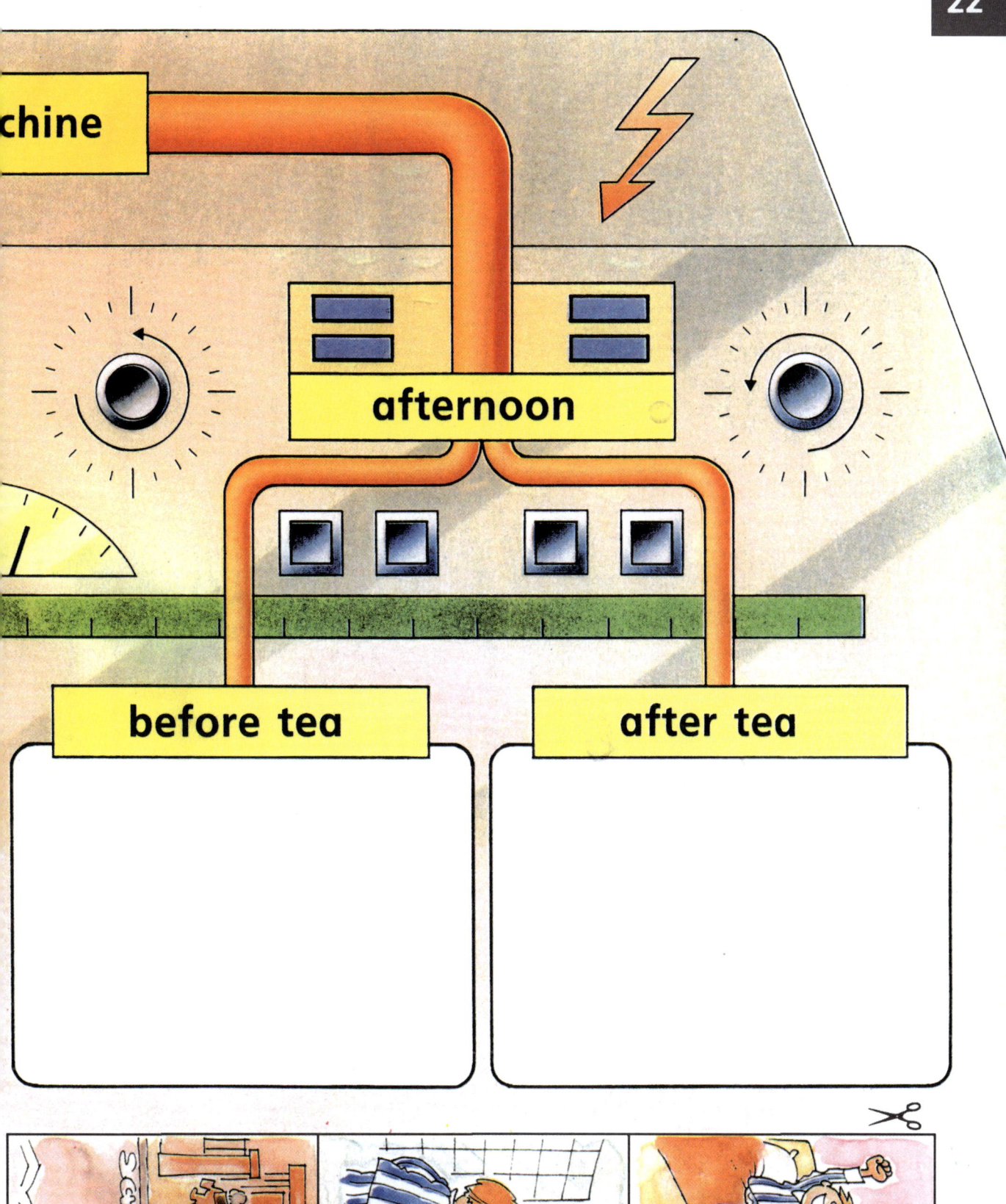

Length: comparison Group work

Shoes

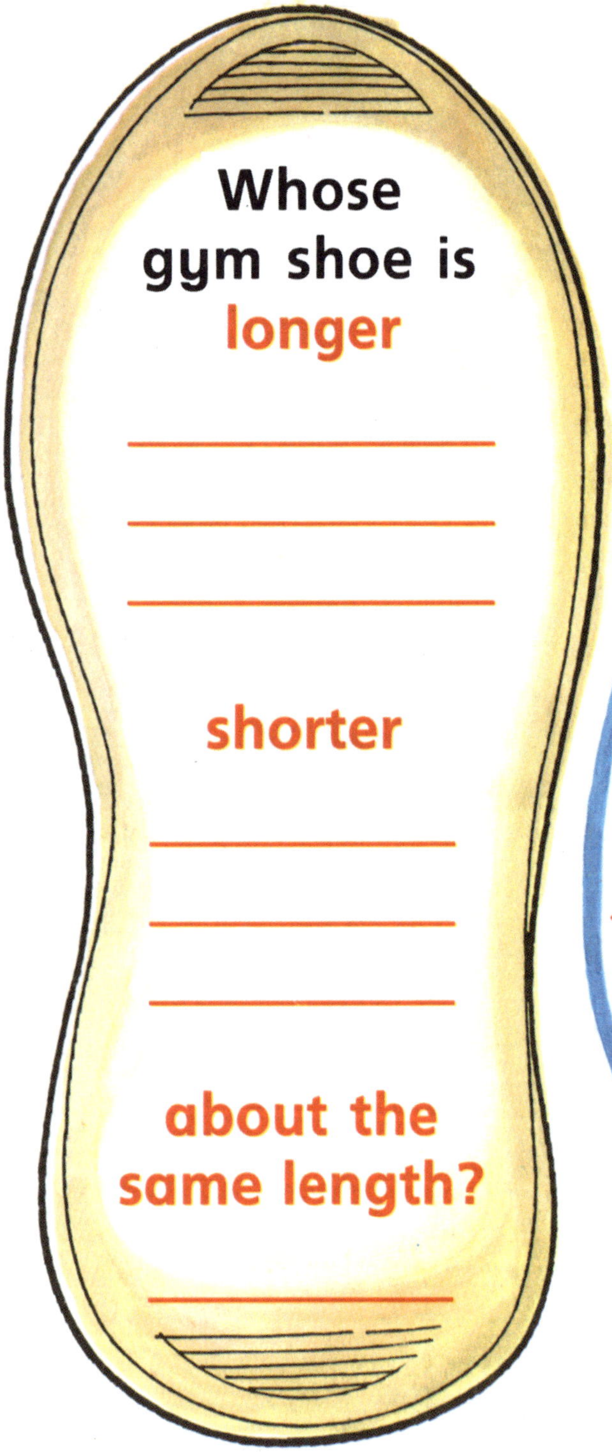

Whose gym shoe is **longer**

shorter

about the same length?

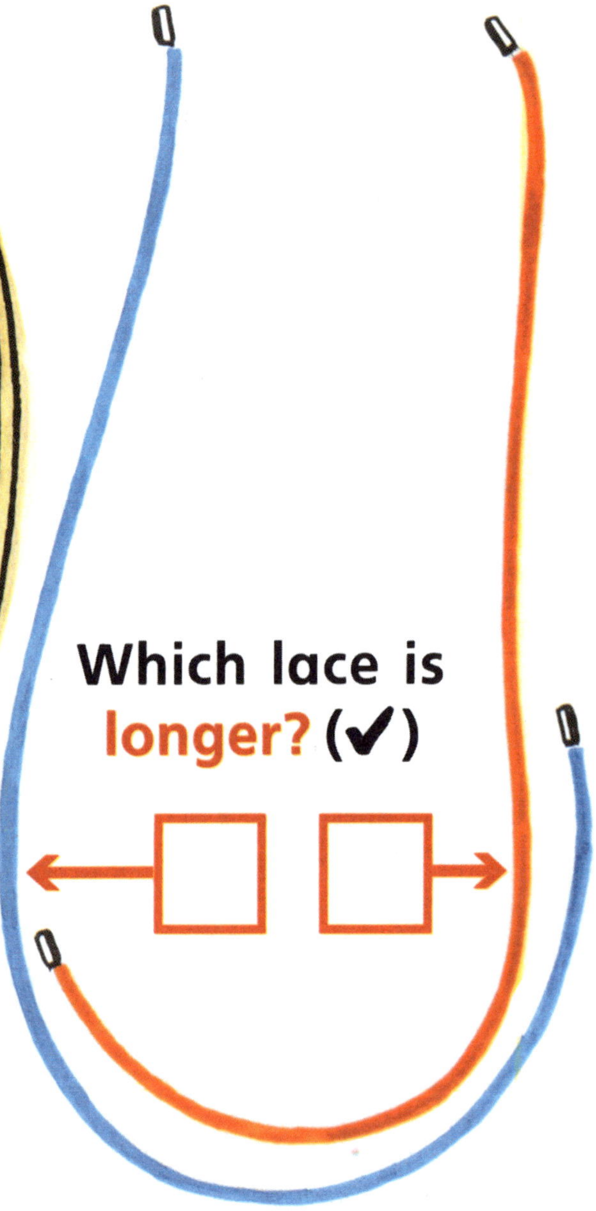

Which lace is **longer?** (✓)

SPMG

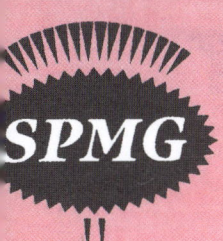

HEINEMANN MATHEMATICS 1

Name

MEASURE WORKBOOK

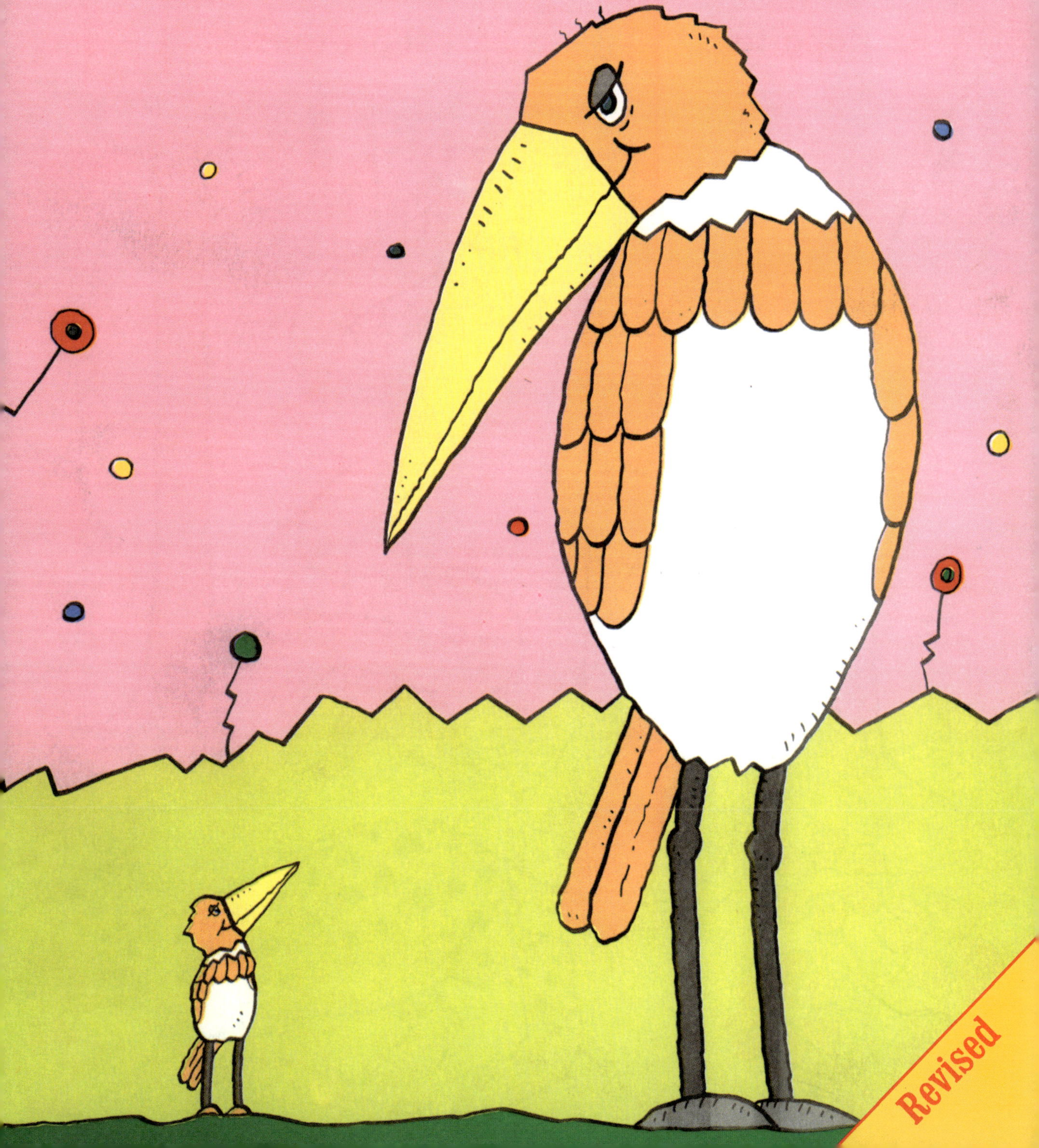

Revised

The Jungle

Length: language

2

How many:

thick trees ☐   thin trees ☐

thick snakes ☐   thin snakes ☐ ?

Time: language Problem solving

3

Day or night?

day night

Colour the sky.

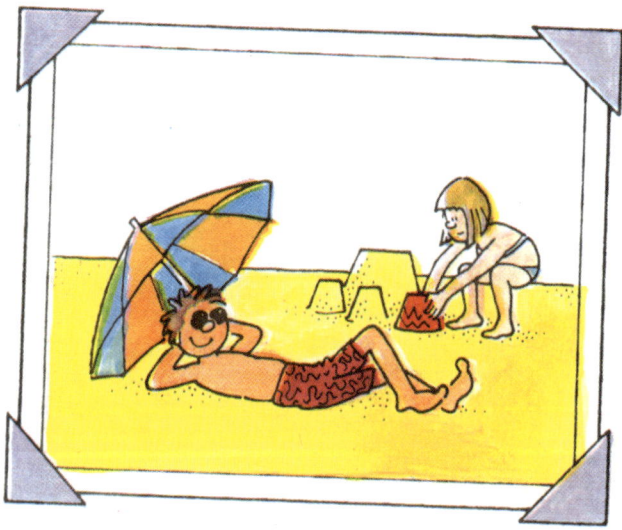 

Problem solving · Time: language

Morning or afternoon?

Colour the morning pictures.

waking up

going home

tea time

taking in the milk

5 Time: language — Problem solving

What happened after?

Colour

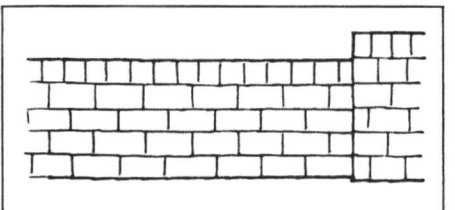

or

or

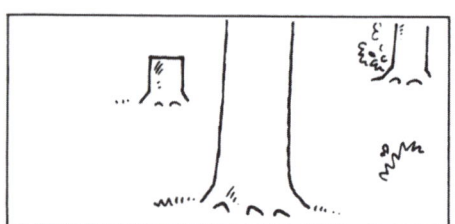

or

Problem solving | **Time: language**

What happened before?

Colour

or

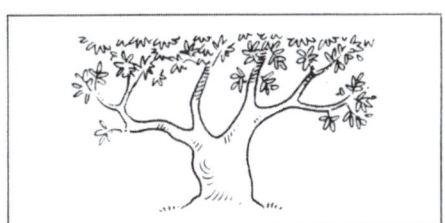

or

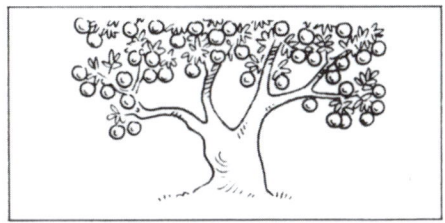

or

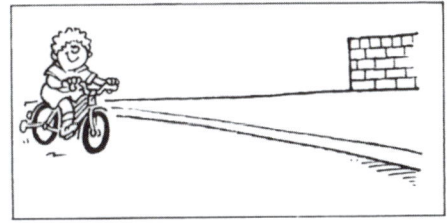

Heavier and lighter

Write **h** for heavier and **l** for lighter.

Weight: comparison

Rabbits

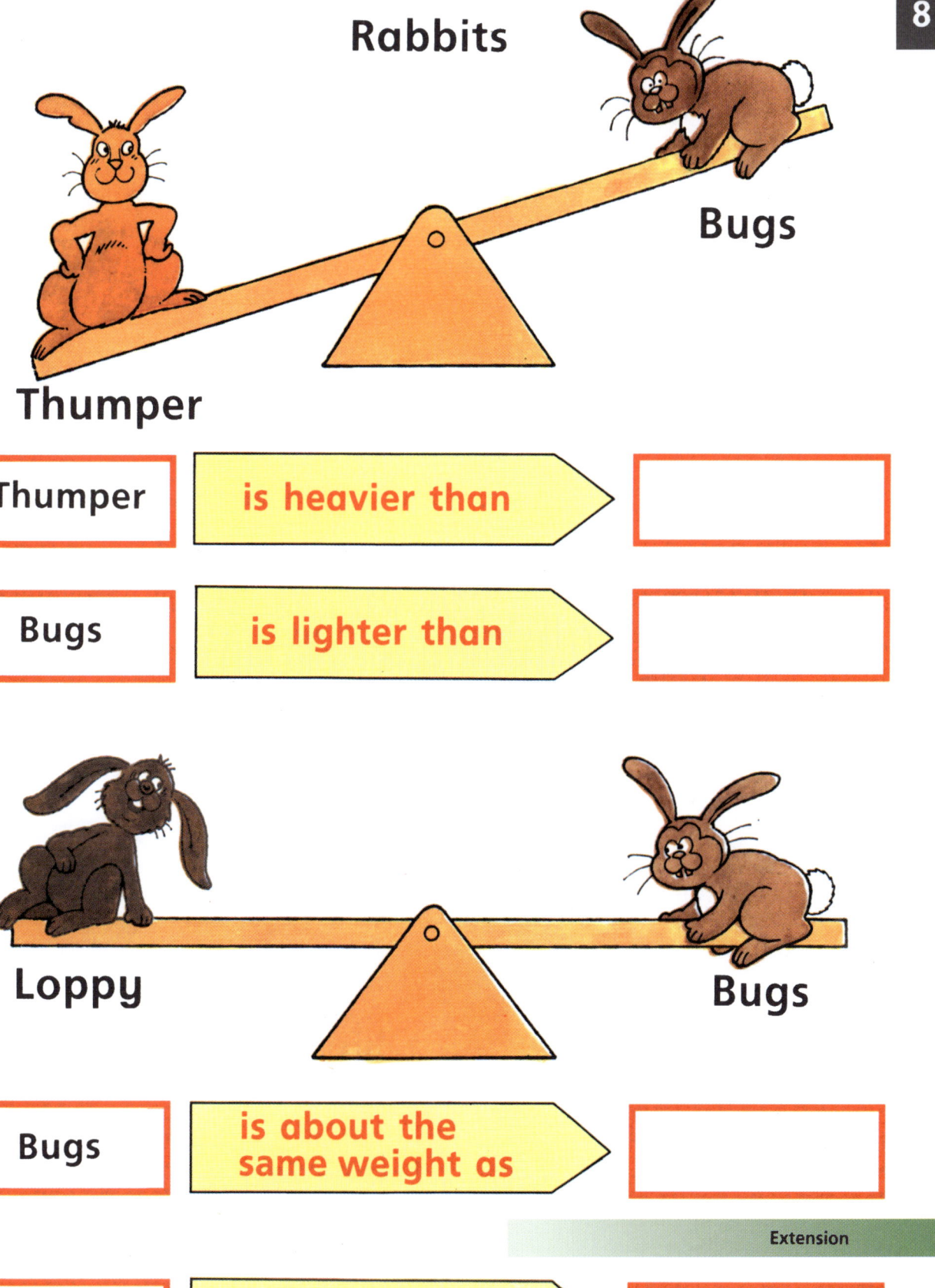

| Thumper | is heavier than | |
| Bugs | is lighter than | |

| Bugs | is about the same weight as | |

Extension

| Loppy | is lighter than | |

About how many cups does each fill?

Draw 🍵

Longer and shorter

Find 2 things **longer** than your thumb.

_____

_____

Find 2 things **shorter** than your shoe.

_____

_____

Length: language

Taller, shorter, thicker, thinner

Find someone who is taller than you.

_____

Find someone who is shorter than you.

_____

Find something thicker than your thumb.

_____

Find something thinner than your little finger.

_____

Longer, shorter, taller
Match

Length: language

14

Mark the **thicker**

Mark the **thinner**

Length: ordering

In your group who has

the longest ✏️ _____

the shortest ✏️ ? _____

Colour the longest 🟥
the shortest 🟦

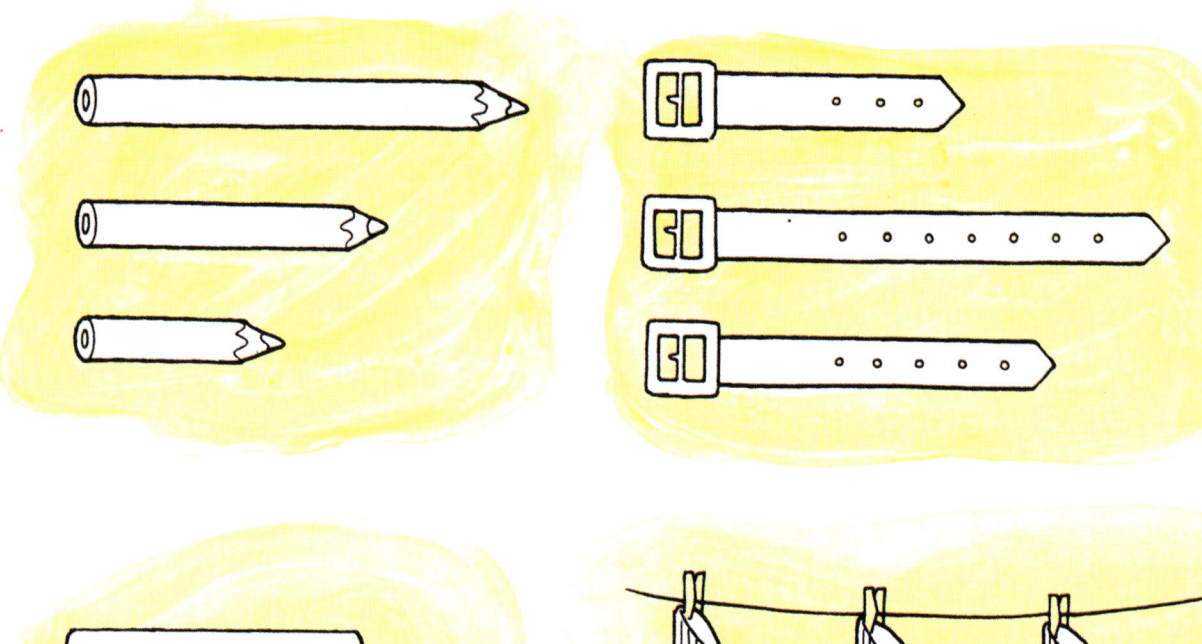

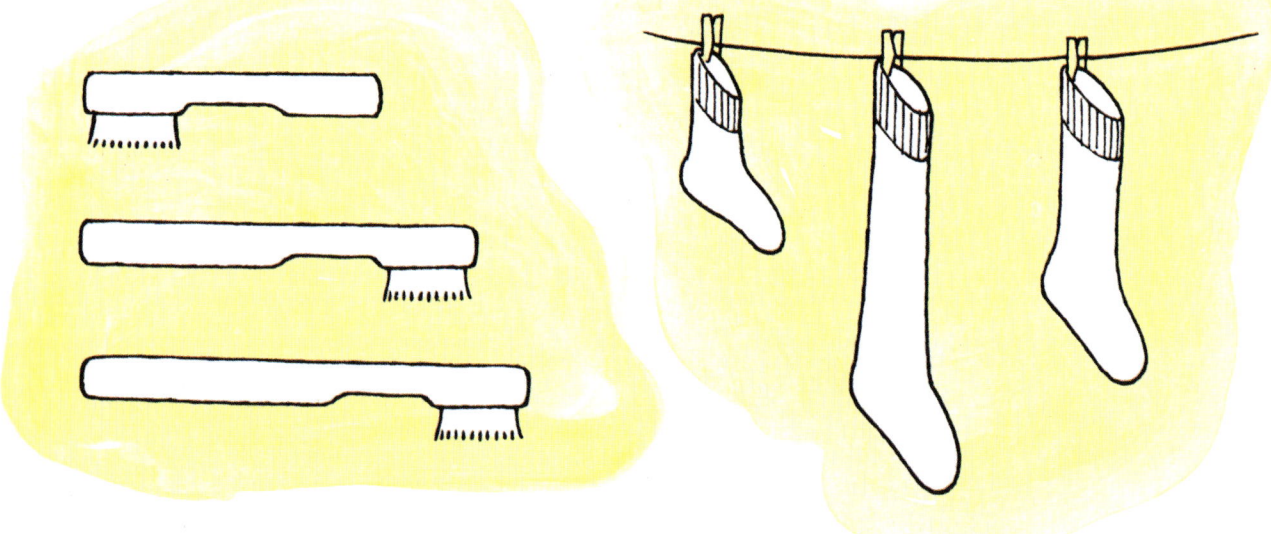

Length: ordering

16

In your group who is

tallest _____

shortest? _____

Colour the tallest
the shortest

What time is it?

Time stories

Time: digital display

What time is it?

☐ o'clock

☐ o'clock

☐ o'clock

☐ o'clock

Match clocks which show the same time.

Bus times

Colour the roads the bus takes.

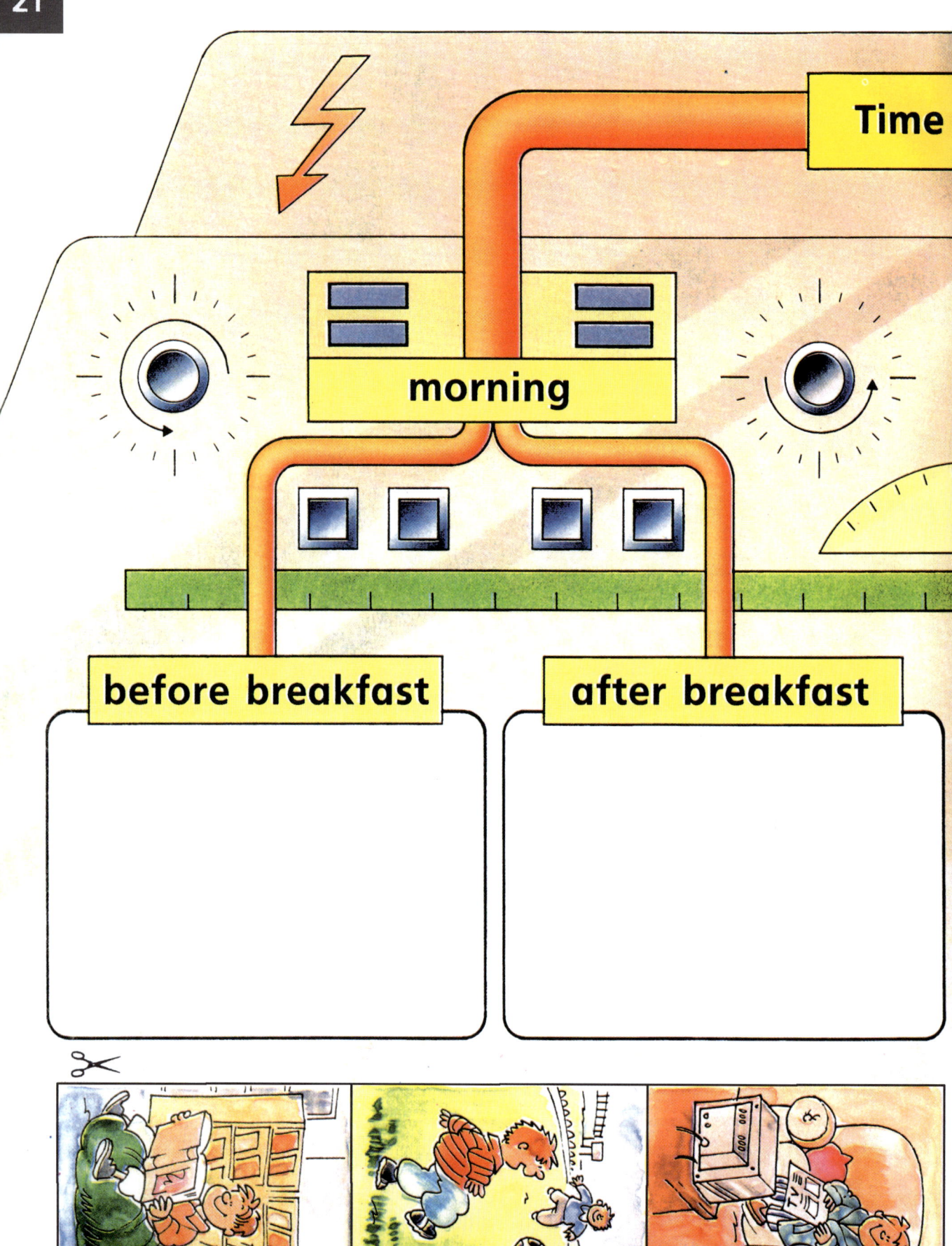

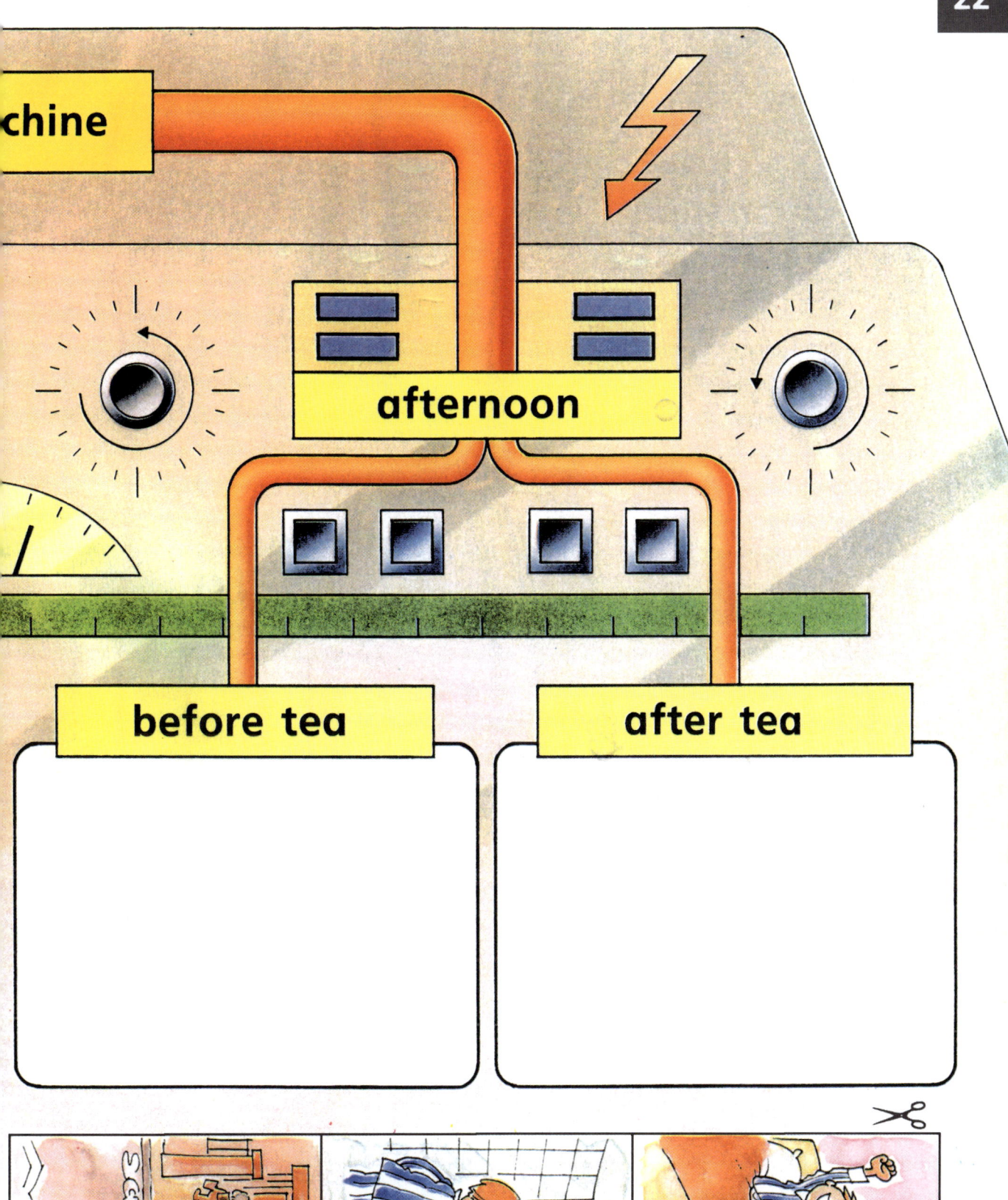

Length: comparison Group work

Shoes

Whose gym shoe is **longer**

_____
_____
_____

shorter

_____
_____
_____

about the same length?

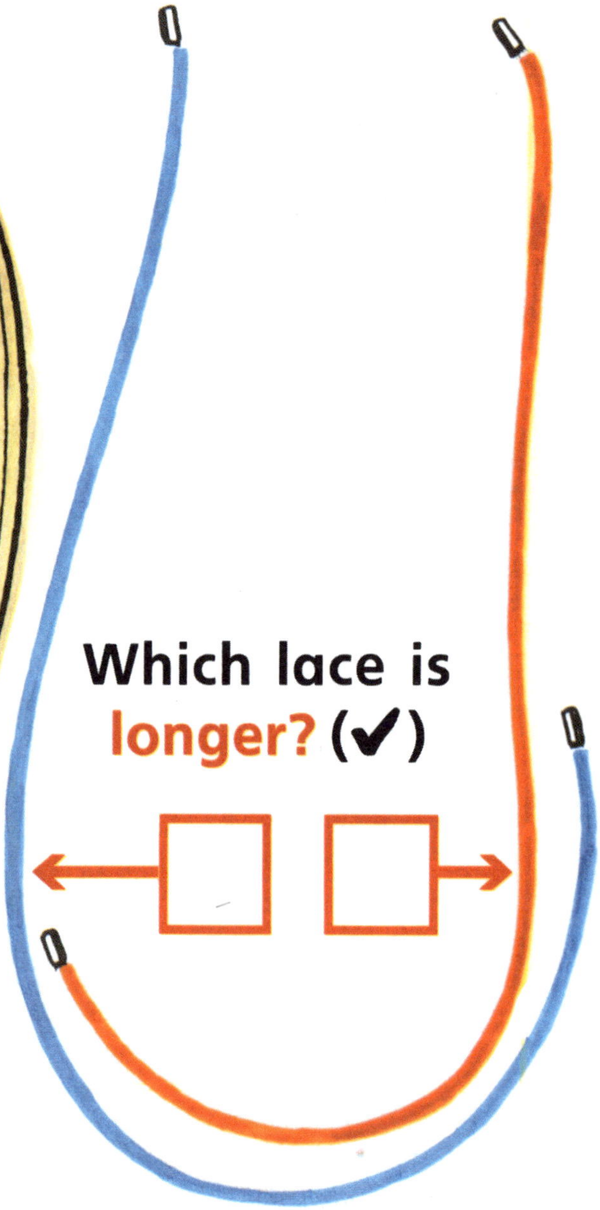

_____

Which lace is **longer?** (✓)

→ ☐   ☐ ←

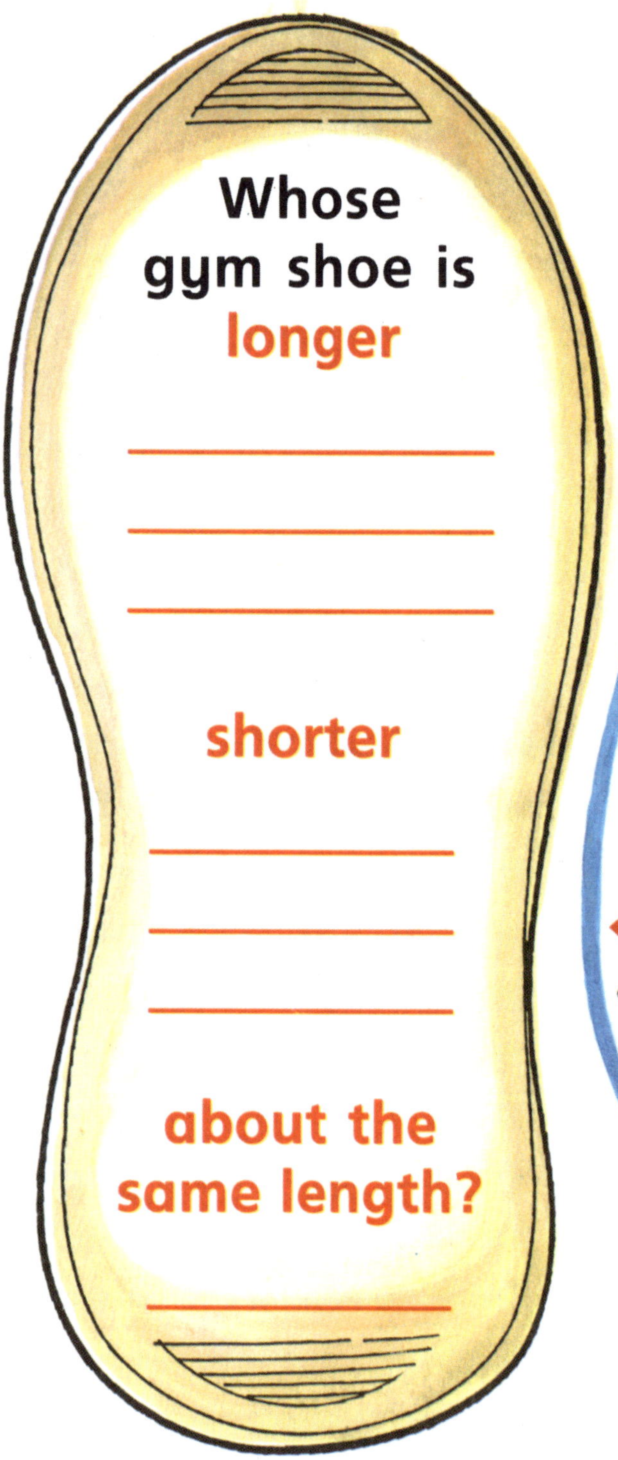

1	2	3	4	5	6	7	8	9	10	11	12	13	14	15	16	17	18	19	20	21	22	23

Heinemann is an imprint of Pearson Education Limited, a company incorporated in England and Wales, having its registered office at Edinburgh Gate, Harlow, Essex, CM20 2JE.
Registered company number: 872828
8 Pack. ISBN 978 0 435 03708 6. Single ISBN 978 0 435 03089 6
© Scottish Primary Mathematics Group 1991.
First published 1991. Revised edition 1995.
Typeset and illustrated by Oxprint Design. Printed in Great Britain by Bell & Bain Ltd, Glasgow

25 30

ISBN 978-0-435030-89-6

HEINEMANN MATHEMATICS 1

Name _____

MEASURE WORKBOOK

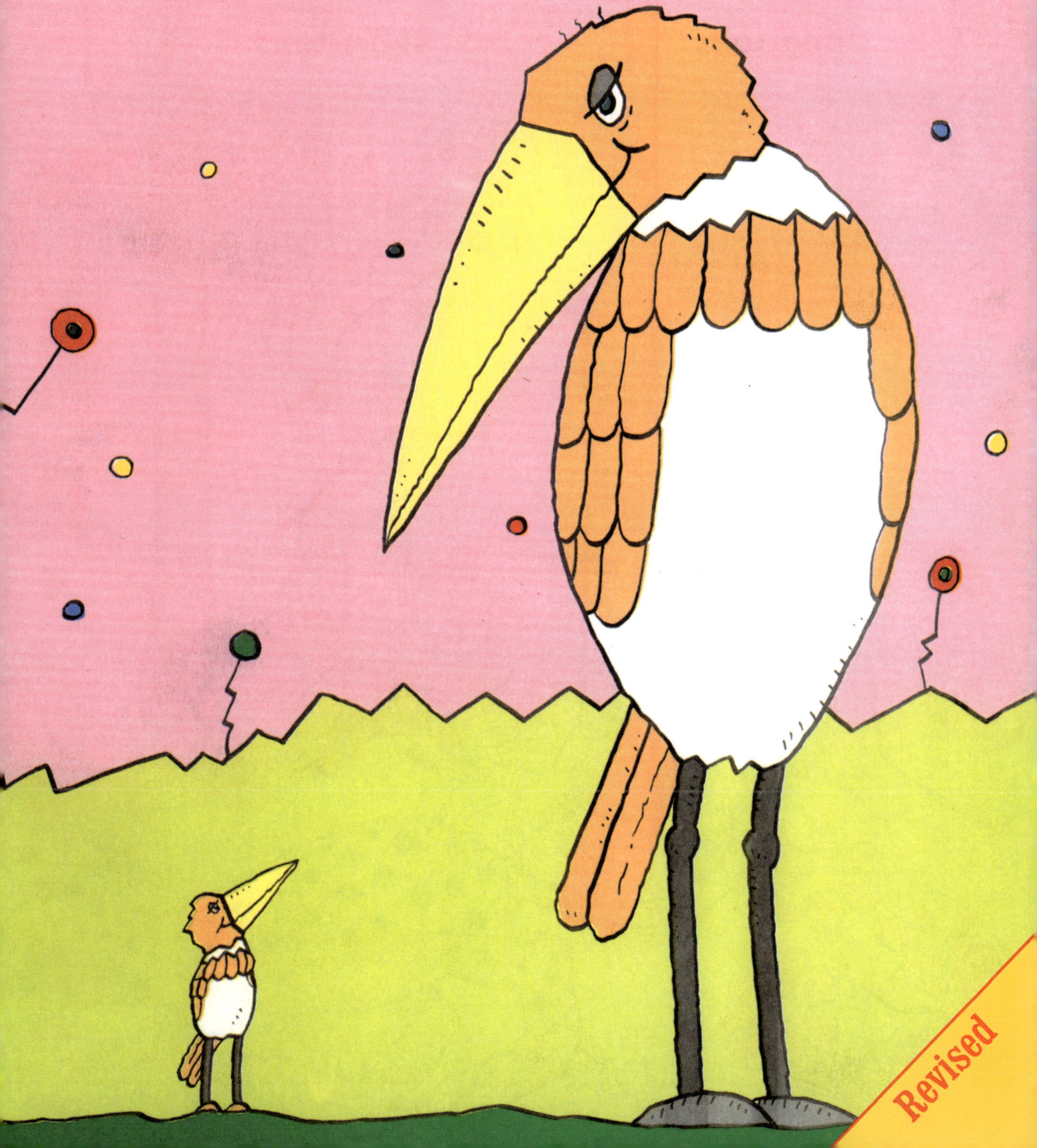

Revised

The Jungle

Length: language

2

How many:

thick trees ☐   thin trees ☐

thick snakes ☐   thin snakes ☐ ?

Day or night?

day night

Colour the sky.

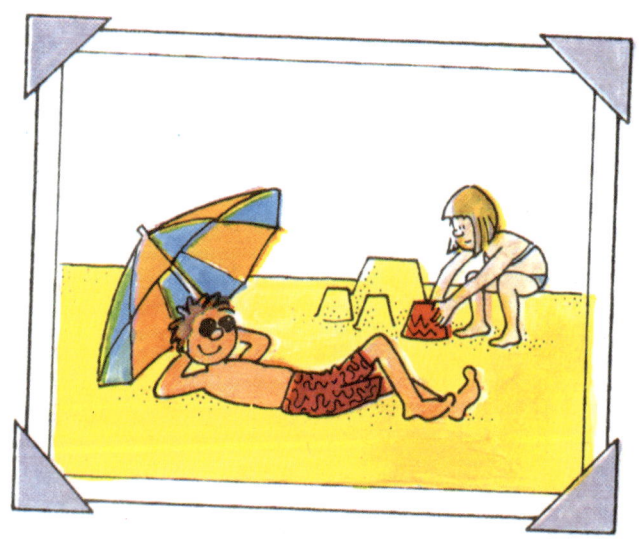 

Problem solving   Time: language

Morning or afternoon?

Colour the morning pictures.

waking up

going home

tea time

taking in the milk

5 Time: language   Problem solving

What happened after?

Colour

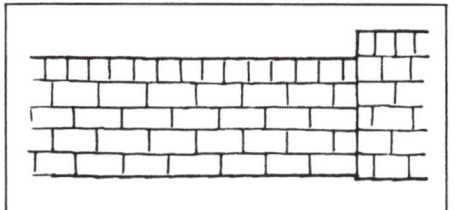

or

or

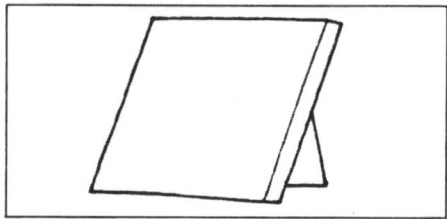

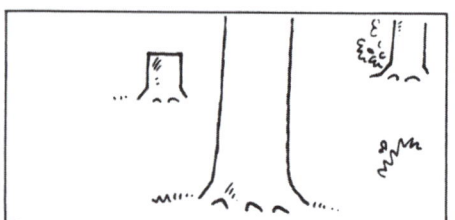

or

Problem solving   Time: language

What happened before?

Colour

or

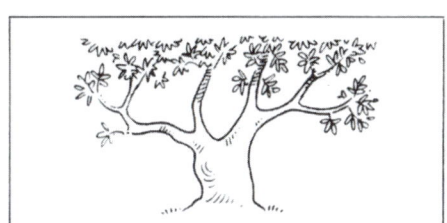

or

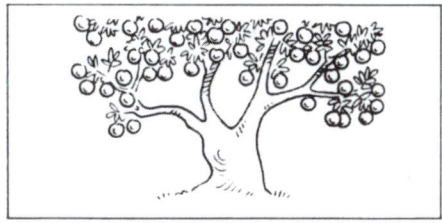

or

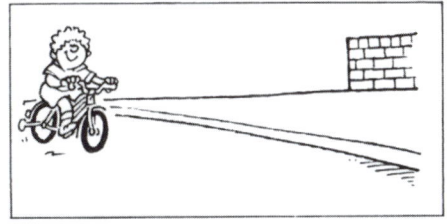

Heavier and lighter

Write [h] for heavier and [l] for lighter.

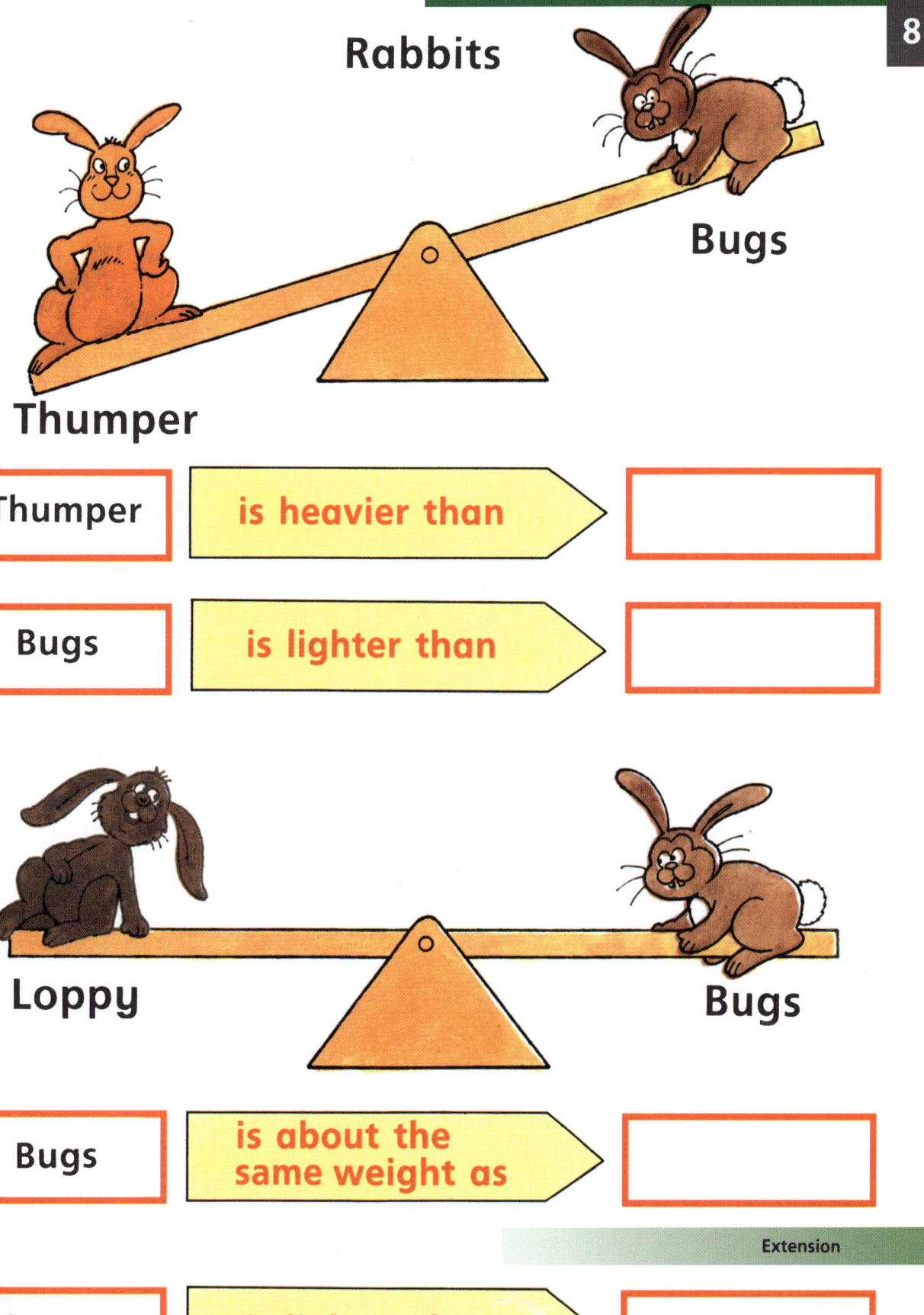

About how many cups does each fill?

Longer and shorter

Find 2 things **longer** than your thumb.

_____

_____

Find 2 things **shorter** than your shoe.

_____

_____

Taller, shorter, thicker, thinner

Find someone who is taller than you.

_____

Find someone who is shorter than you.

_____

Find something thicker than your thumb.

_____

Find something thinner than your little finger.

_____

Length: language

14

Mark the thicker

Mark the thinner

Length: ordering

15

In your group who has

the longest ✏️ _____

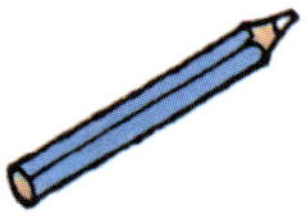

the shortest ✏️ ? _____

Colour the longest 🔴
the shortest 🔵

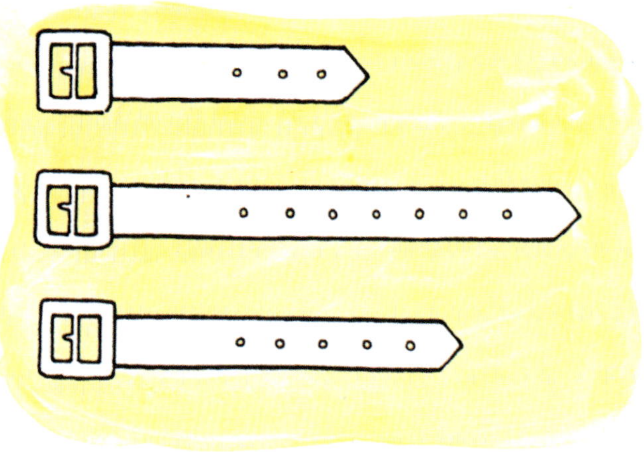

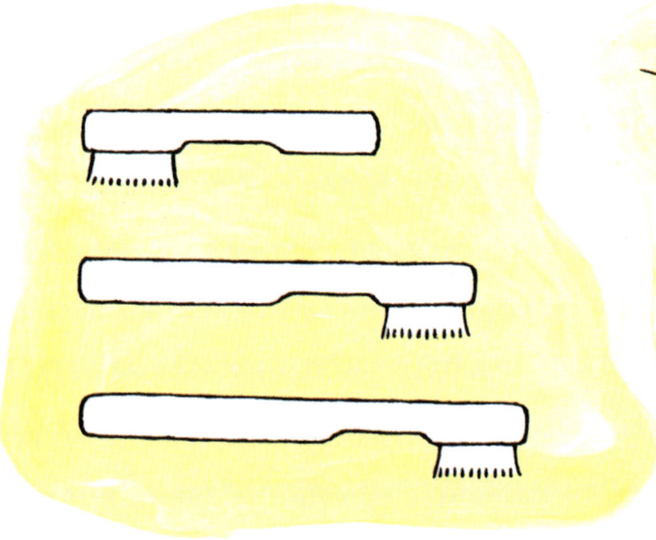

Length: ordering

16

In your group who is

tallest _____

shortest? _____

Colour the tallest
 the shortest

Time stories

Time: digital display

What time is it?

☐ o'clock

☐ o'clock

☐ o'clock

☐ o'clock

Match clocks which show the same time.

Problem solving Time

Bus times

Colour the roads the bus takes.

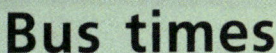

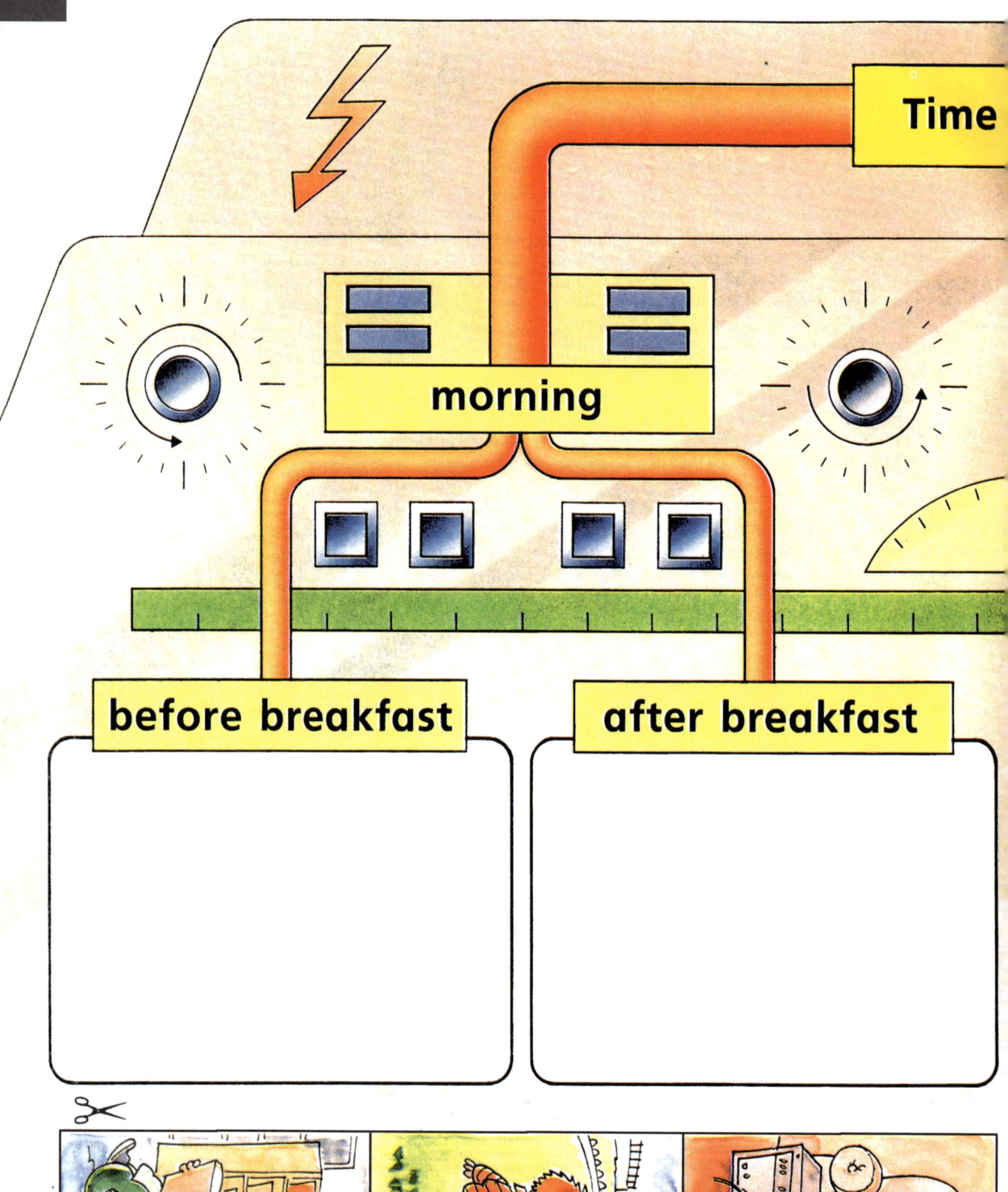

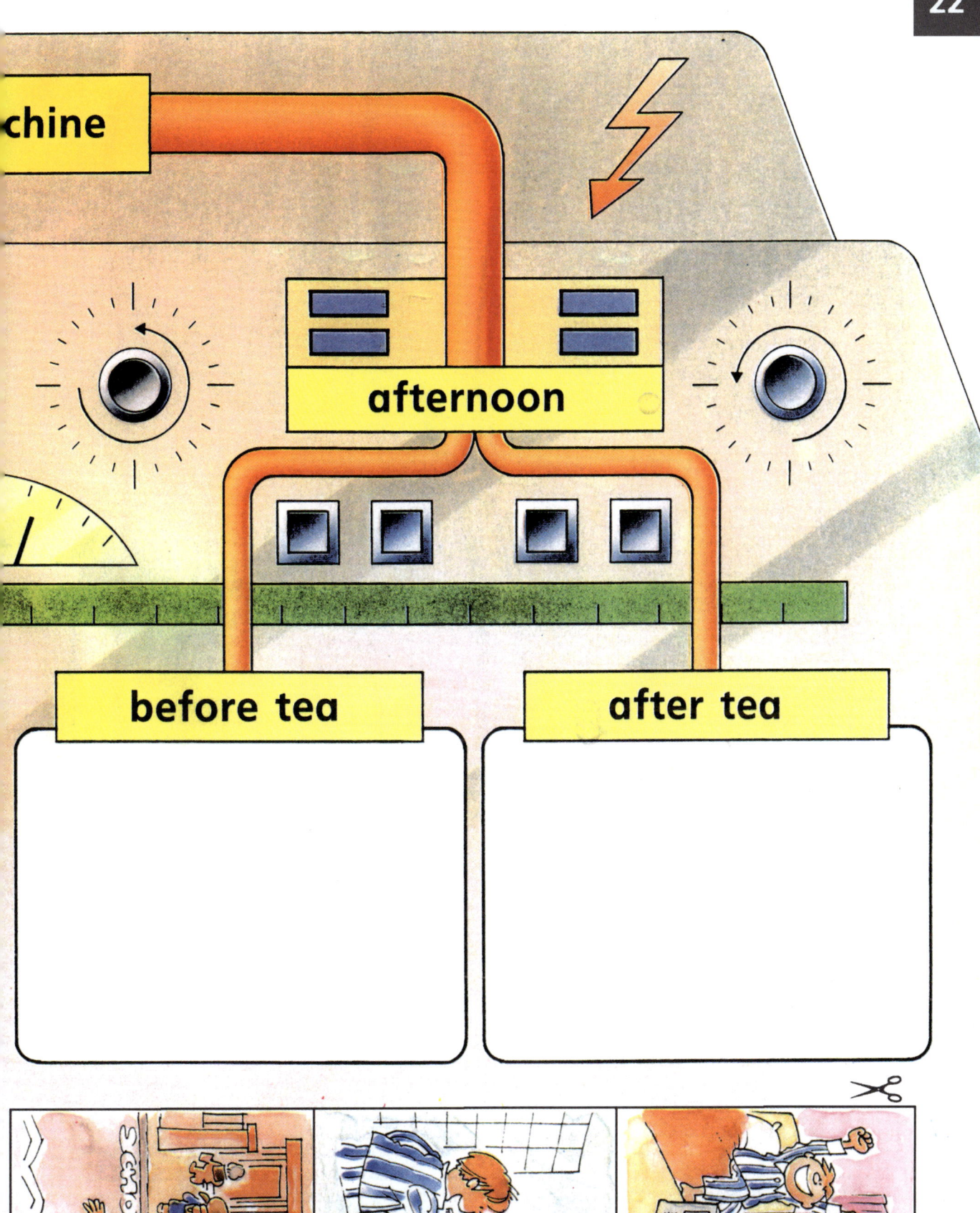

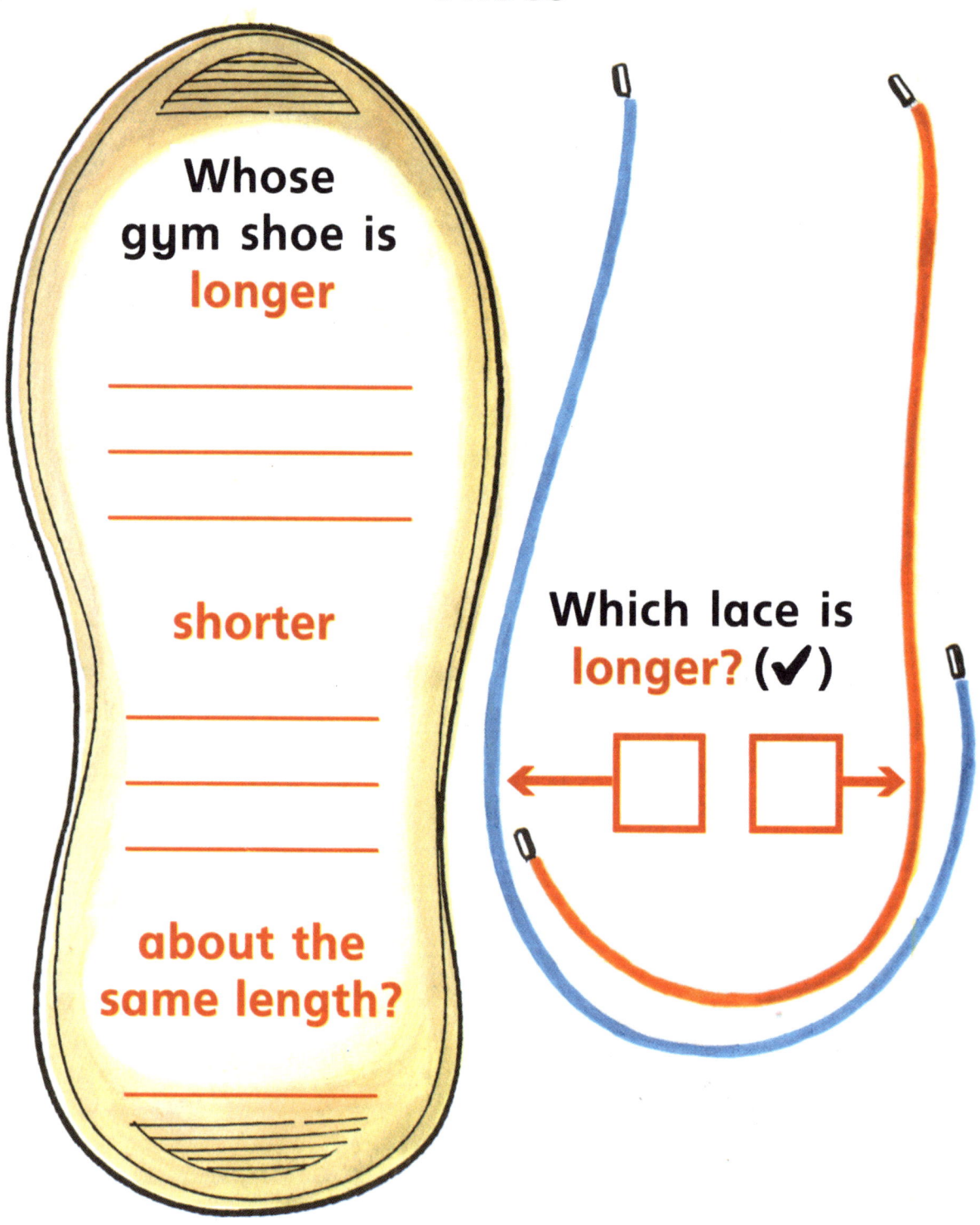

HEINEMANN MATHEMATICS 1

Name _____

MEASURE WORKBOOK

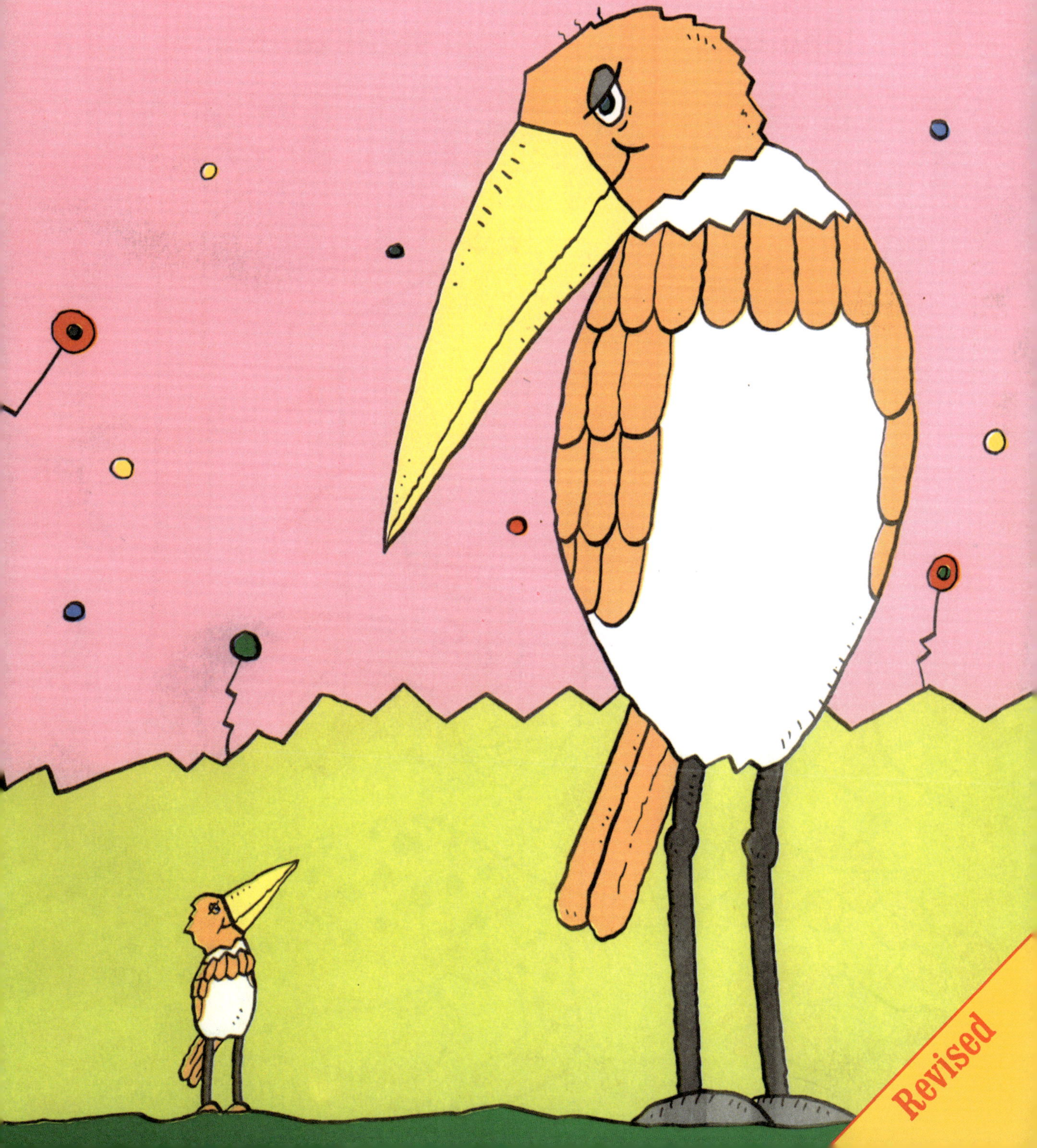

Revised

Length: language

CARDS   Length   Cards 1 to 6

How many:
- tall flowers ☐
- short flowers ☐
- long tails ☐
- short tails ☐ ?

The Jungle

How many:

thick trees ☐   thin trees ☐

thick snakes ☐   thin snakes ☐ ?

Day or night?

day night

Colour the sky.

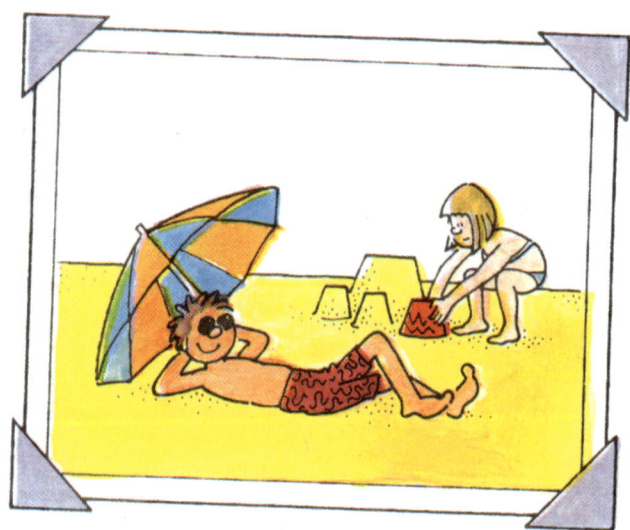 

Problem solving Time: language

Morning or afternoon?

Colour the morning pictures.

waking up

going home

tea time

taking in the milk

What happened after?

Time: language — Problem solving

Colour

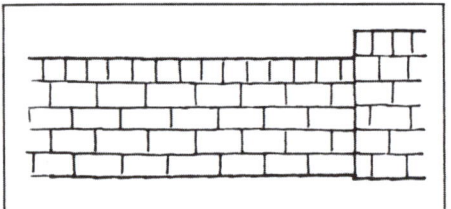

or

or

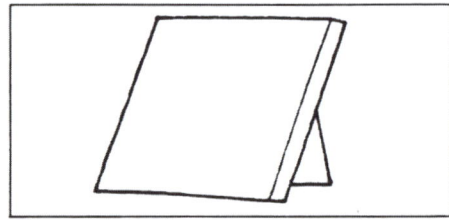

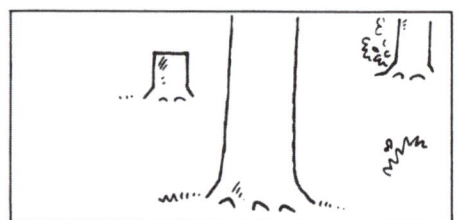

or

Problem solving — **Time: language**

What happened before?

Colour

or

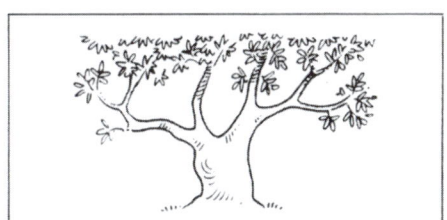
or
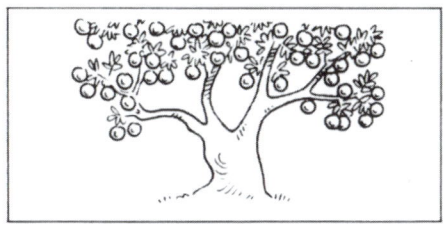

or
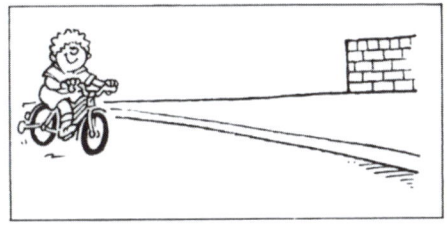

Heavier and lighter

Write [h] for heavier and [l] for lighter.

Weight: comparison

8

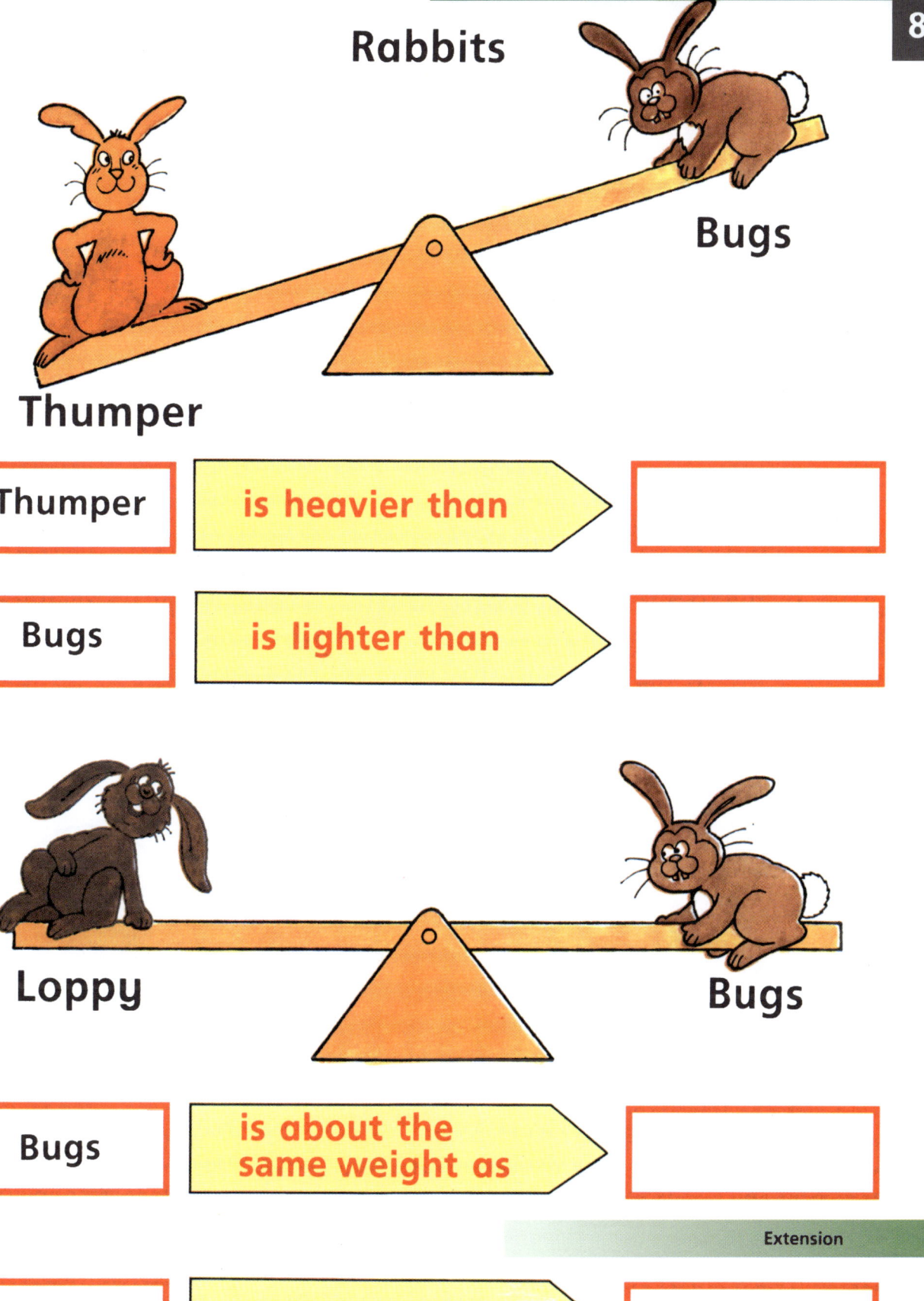

Rabbits

Thumper — Bugs

| Thumper | is heavier than | |
| Bugs | is lighter than | |

Loppy — Bugs

| Bugs | is about the same weight as | |

Extension

| Loppy | is lighter than | |

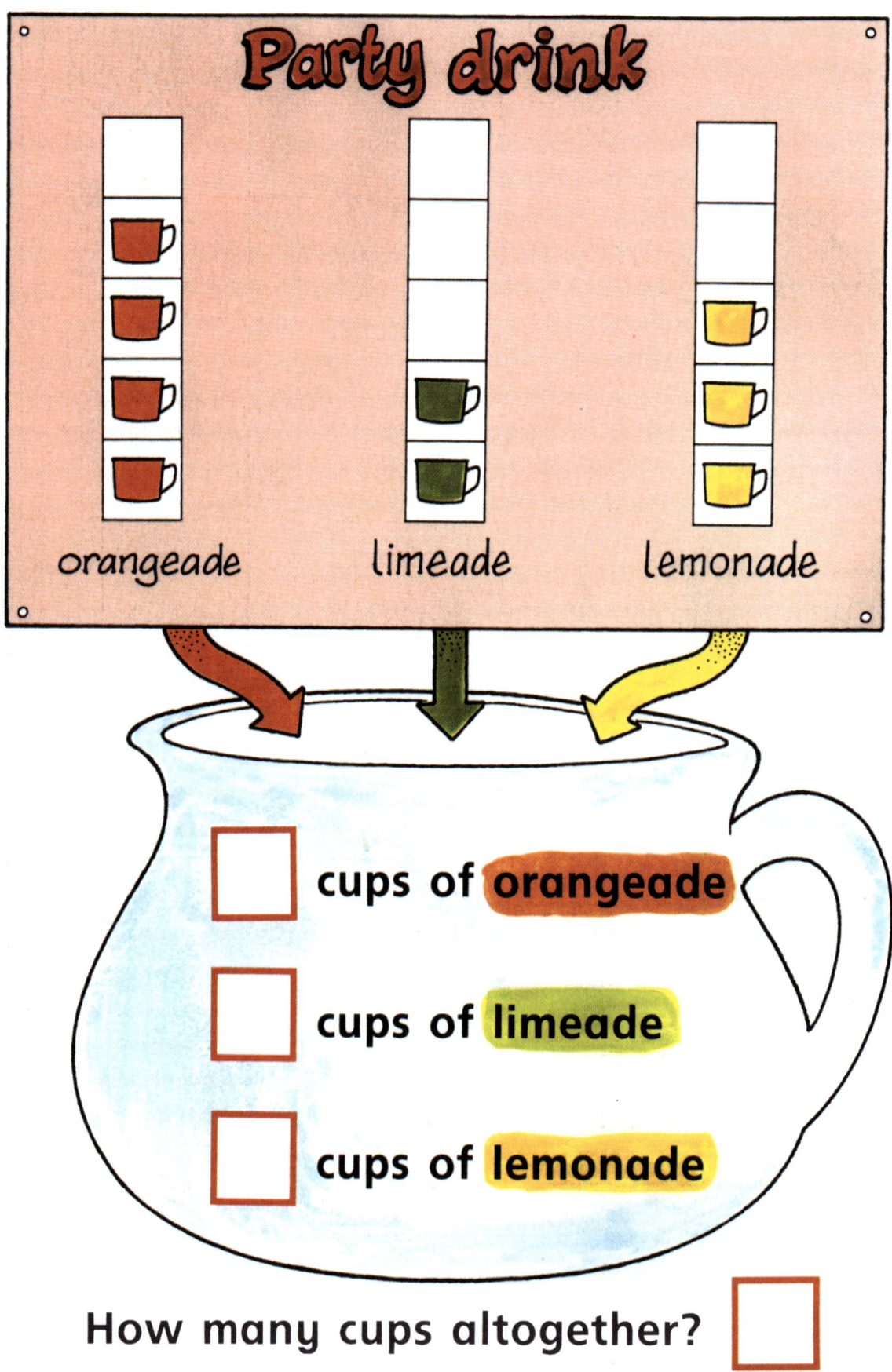

About how many cups does each fill?

Draw 🥣

Length: language

Longer and shorter

Find 2 things **longer** than your thumb.

_____

_____

Find 2 things **shorter** than your shoe.

_____

_____

Length: language

Taller, shorter, thicker, thinner

Find someone who is **taller** than you.

_____

Find someone who is **shorter** than you.

_____

Find something **thicker** than your thumb.

_____

Find something **thinner** than your little finger.

_____

Length: language

Mark the **thicker**

Mark the **thinner**

Length: ordering

In your group who has

the longest ✏️ _____

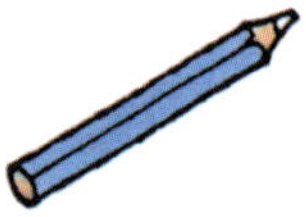

the shortest ✏️ ? _____

Colour the longest 🔴 
the shortest 🔵

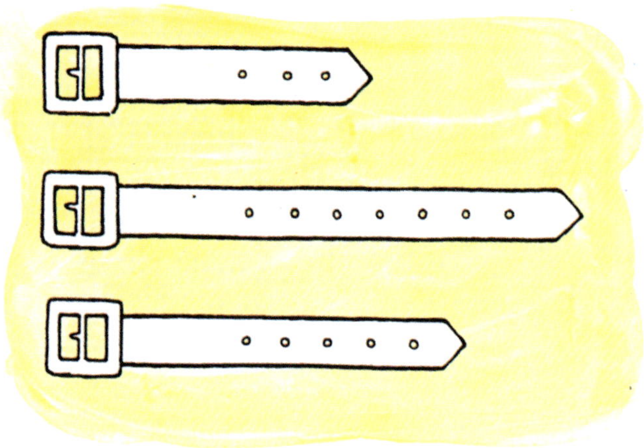

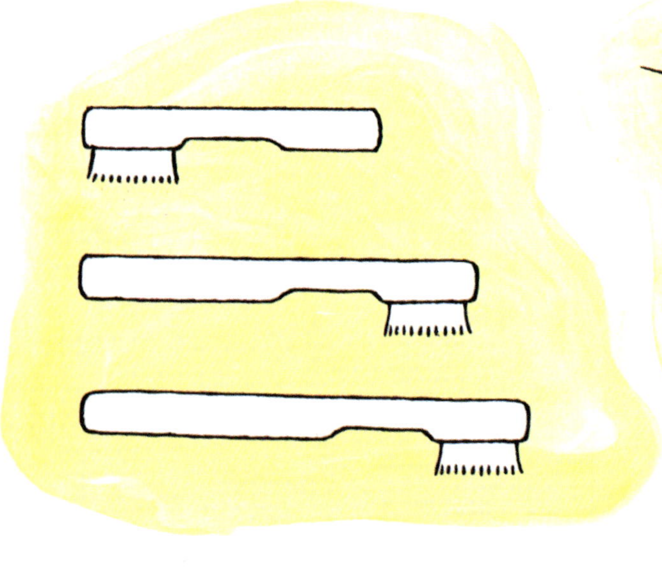

Length: ordering

16

In your group who is

tallest _____

shortest? _____

Colour the tallest
the shortest

Time stories

Time: digital display

What time is it?

☐ o'clock

☐ o'clock

☐ o'clock

☐ o'clock

Match clocks which show the same time.

Problem solving — Time

Bus times

Colour the roads the bus takes.

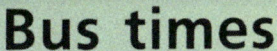

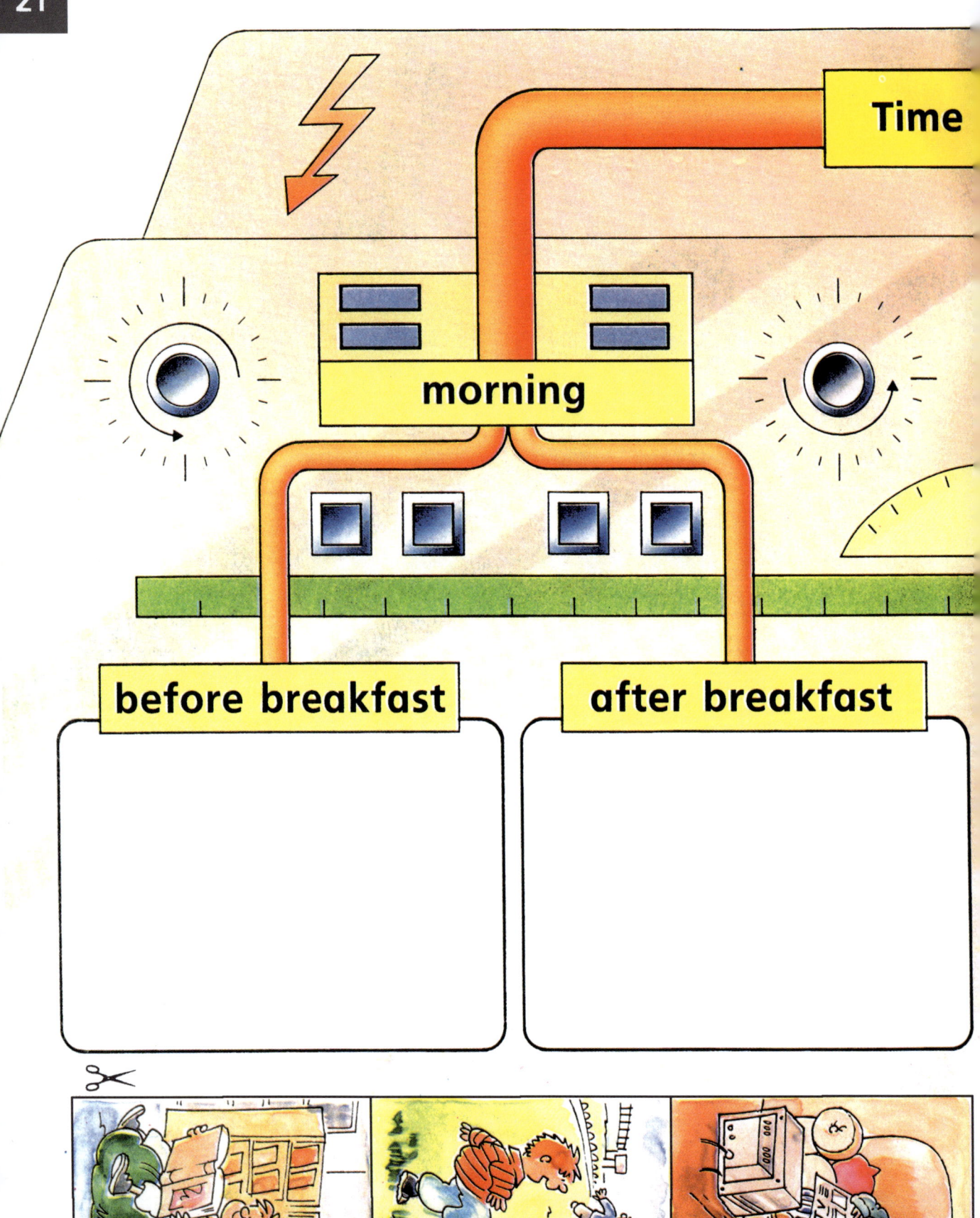

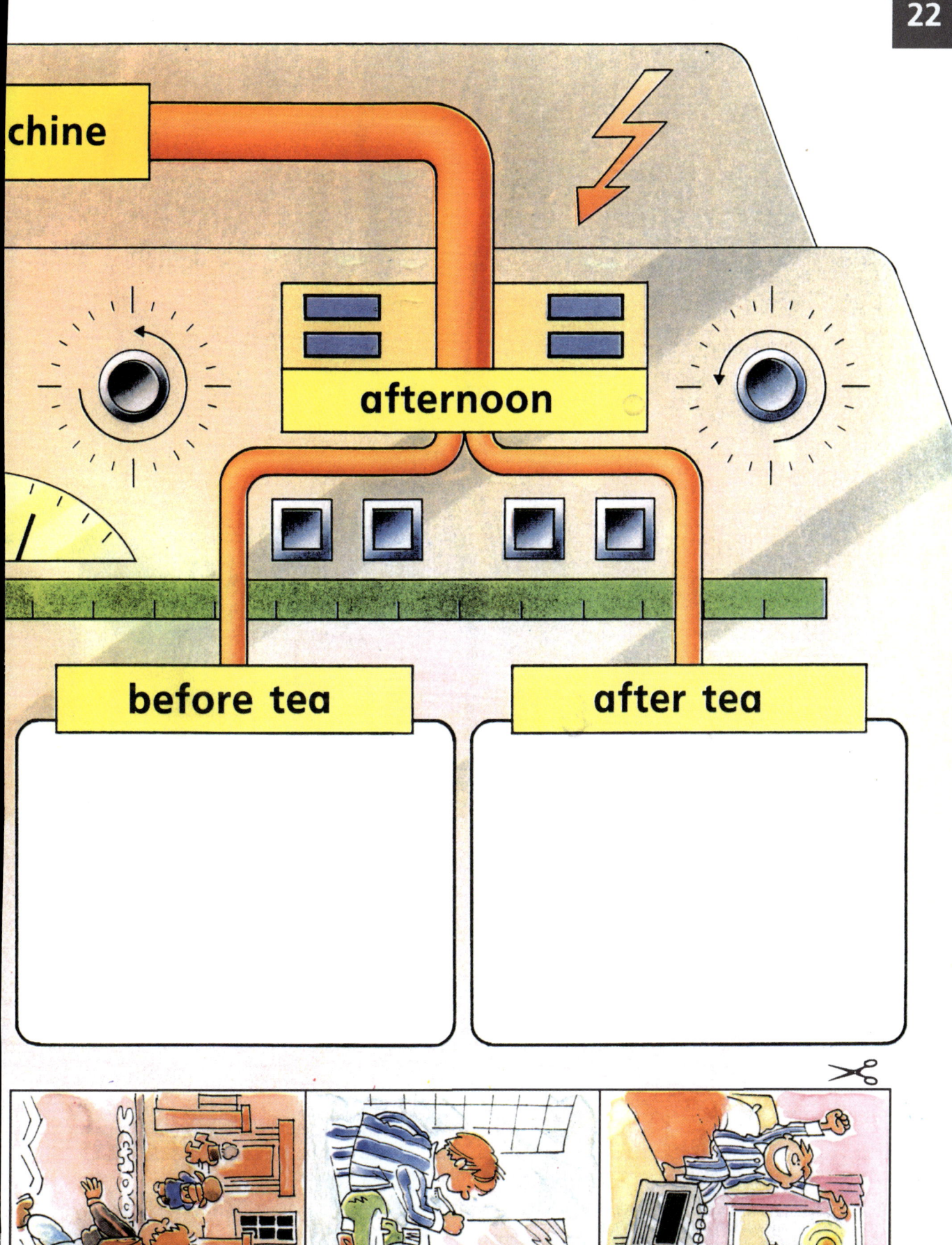

Length: comparison   Group work

Shoes

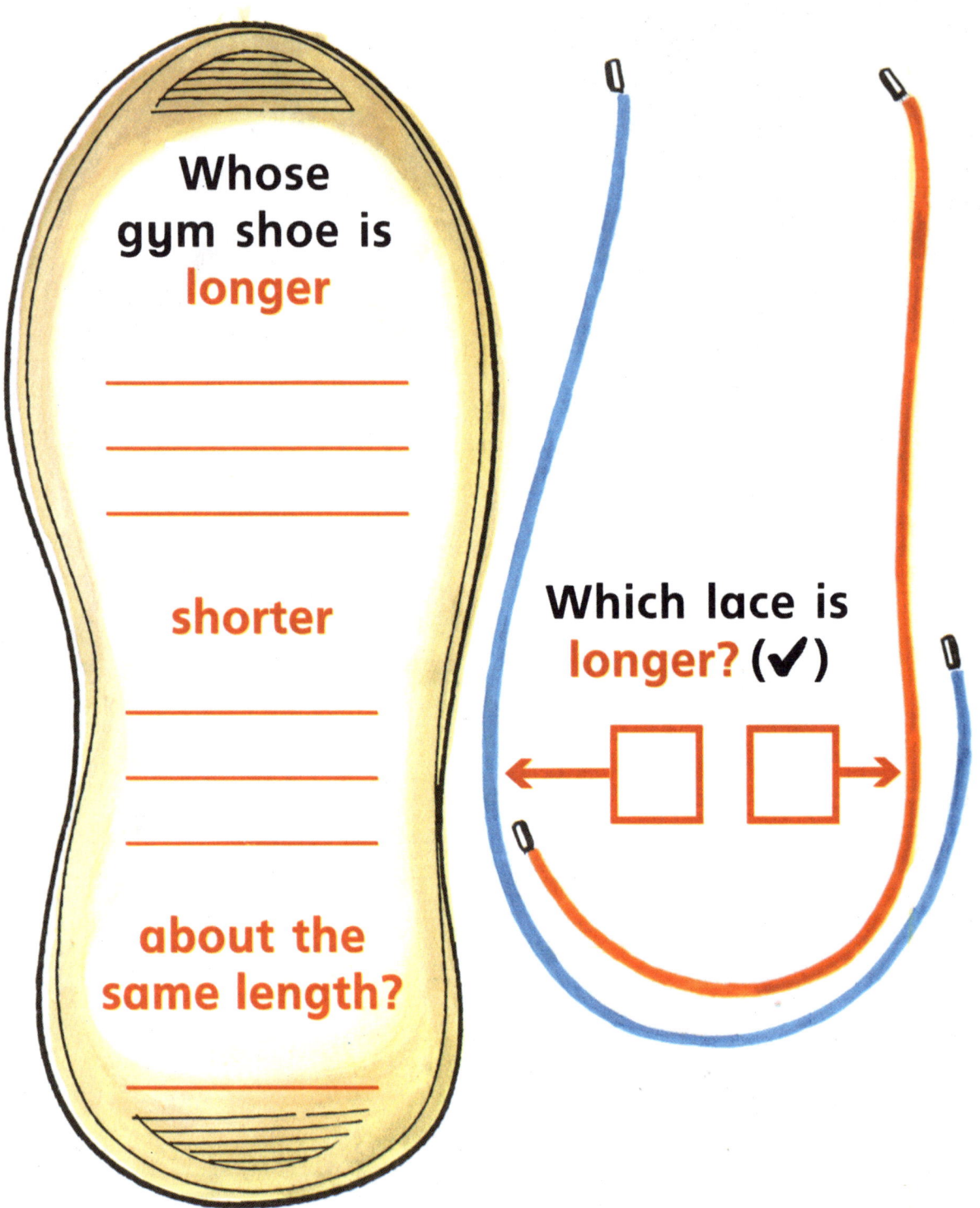

Whose gym shoe is **longer**

shorter

about the same length?

Which lace is **longer?** (✔)